RUSS SHIPTONS
Rock & Pop Guitar
Songbook 1

Contents

Note: The songs in this book are taken from "Russ Shiptons Rock & Pop Guitar" Coursebooks 1 & 2. The Coursebooks and matching cassettes include the analysis and demonstration of chords, rhythm patterns and techniques needed to play the accompaniments effectively (see back cover)

First Published 1986
© International Music Publications

Exclusive Distributors
International Music Publications
Southend Road, Woodford Green,
Essex IG8 8HN, England.

Printed in England by JB Offset (Marks Tey) Limited
Marks Tey, Essex.

SATISFACTION (I Can't Get No)

Words and Music by
MICK JAGGER and KEITH RICHARD

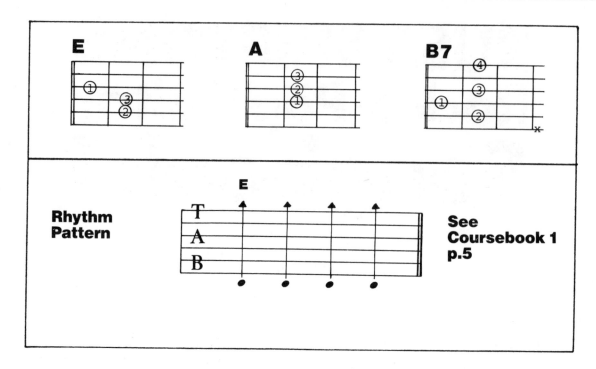

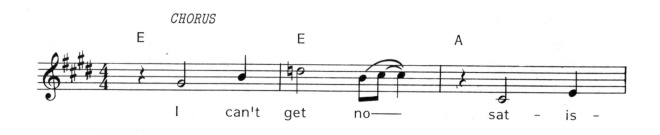

I can't get no—— sat - is -

fact - ion.—— I can't get no — sat - is -

fact - ion.'Cos I try, and I try, and I try, and I

try.—— I can't get no, I can't get no. . .

Westminster Music Ltd, 19/20 Poland Street, London W1V 3DD

1,2 & 3 When I'm— 1. driv - in' in my— car, and that—
              2. watch- in' my T.— V., and that—
              3. rid - in' round the— world, and I'm——

man comes on the ra - di - o, and he's tell-in' me more and
man comes on to tell me how white my shirts can
do - in' this, and I'm sign-in' that, and I'm tryin' to make some

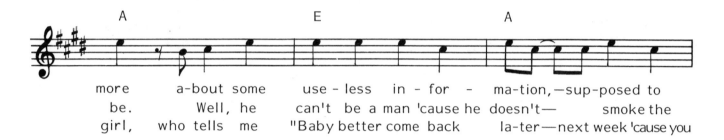

more a-bout some use - less in - for - ma-tion,—sup-posed to
be. Well, he can't be a man 'cause he doesn't— smoke the
girl, who tells me "Baby better come back la-ter—next week 'cause you

fire my im-ag - in - a-tion.) I can't— get no,
same cig-ar-ettes as me. }
see I'm on a los - ing streak.)

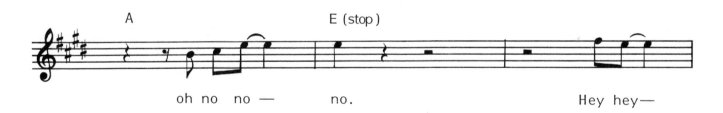

oh no no — no. Hey hey—

hey. — That's what I— say. —

IF I SAID YOU HAVE A BEAUTIFUL BODY

Words and Music
by DAVID BELLAMY

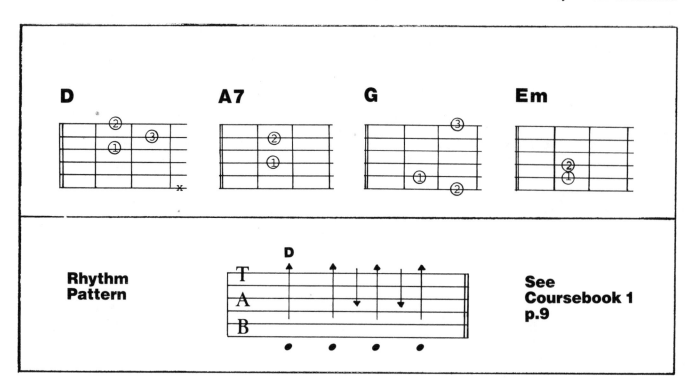

If I said you have a beau-ti-ful

bo-dy, would you hold it a - gainst me?

If I swore you were an an-gel, would you

treat me like the dev-il to - night? ———

If I was dy-ing of thirst,—would your flow-ing love come

quench me? If I said you have a beau- ti – ful

bod- y, would you hold it a – gainst me?

VERSE

Now we could talk all— night a -bout the wea-ther.—

Could tell you 'bout my friends out on the

coast. I could ask a

lot of cra— zy ques-tions,—

or ask you what I real-ly— want— to know.—

HELLO MARYLOU (GOODBYE HEART)

Words and Music
by GENE PITNEY

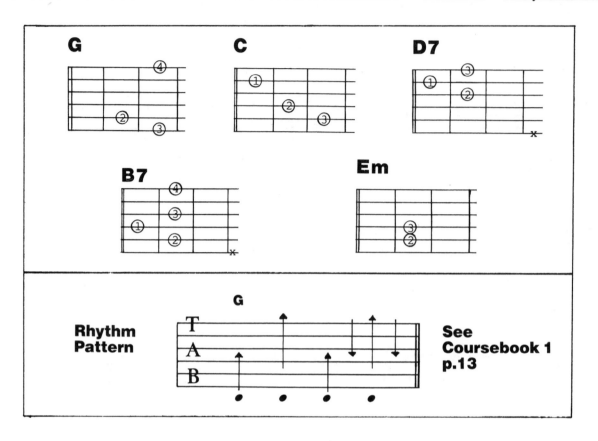

Rhythm Pattern

See Coursebook 1 p.13

CHORUS

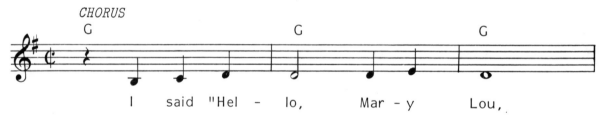

I said "Hel - lo, Mar - y Lou,

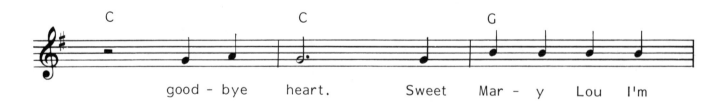

good - bye heart. Sweet Mar - y Lou I'm

so in love with you. I

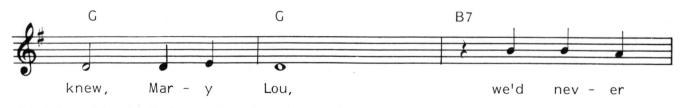

knew, Mar - y Lou, we'd nev - er

7

part, so hel - lo Mar - y Lou, good-bye heart."

VERSE

1. You passed me by one sun - ny day,——
2. I saw your lips, I heard your voice,—— Be-

Flashed those big brown eyes my way, and oo I want - ed
lieve me I just had no choice, wild hors - es could - n't

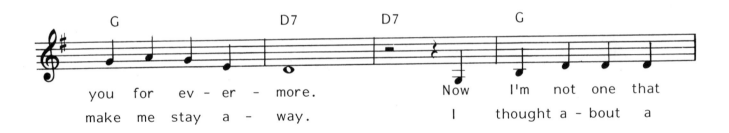

you for ev - er - more. Now I'm not one that
make me stay a - way. I thought a - bout a

gets a-round,— I swear my feet stuck to the ground, and
moon - lit night,— My arms a - bout you good an' tight, that's

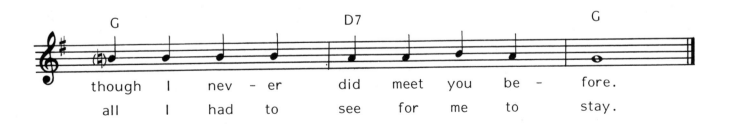

though I nev - er did meet you be - fore.
all I had to see for me to stay.

SONG SUNG BLUE

Words and Music
by NEIL DIAMOND

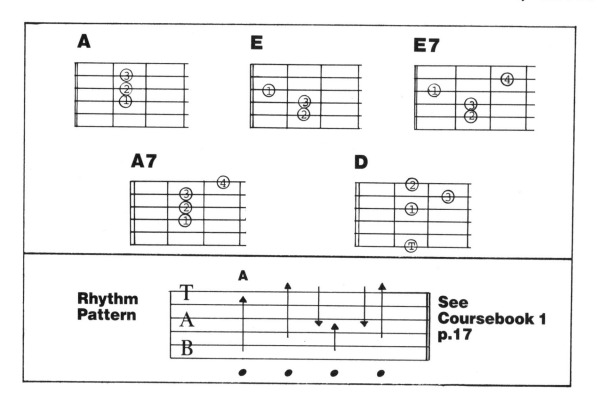

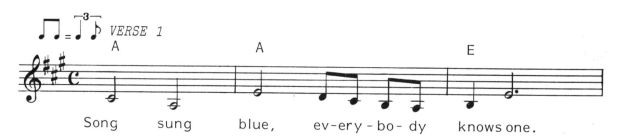

VERSE 1

Song   sung   blue,   ev-ery-bo-dy   knows one.

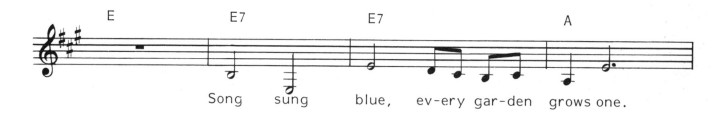

Song   sung   blue,   ev-ery gar-den   grows one.

Me and   you are sub-ject   to   the

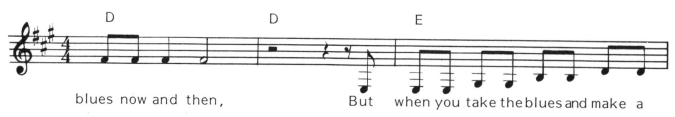

blues now and then,   But   when you take the blues and make a

Warner Bros Music Ltd, 17 Berners Street, London W1

song,　you sing them　out　a - gain, —　　　　　Sing them

VERSE 2

out　a-gain. ————　Song　sung　blue,　weep-in' like a

wil-low. —　　　Song　sung　blue, sleep-in' on my

pil - low.　　Fun-ny— thing, but you can　sing it with a

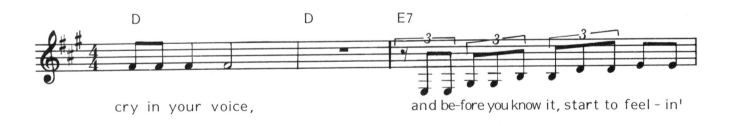

cry in your voice,　　and be-fore you know it, start to feel-in'

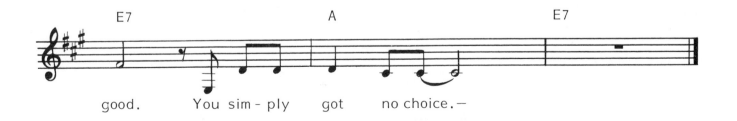

good.　You sim - ply　got　no choice. —

SUMMERTIME AGAIN

Words and Music
by RUSS SHIPTON

ice would not melt, but your sun-shine would ease my
keep me warm, you could or - der the seasons to

pain. Yes, if you come back to me,———
change. So for - get all I said, come clear my

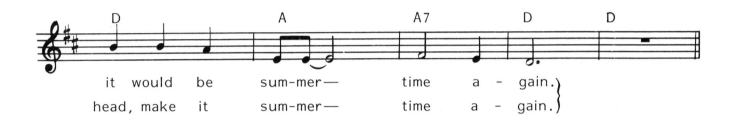

it would be sum-mer— time a - gain.)
head, make it sum-mer— time a - gain.)

CHORUS

Sum-mer— time a - gain.— Sum-mer—

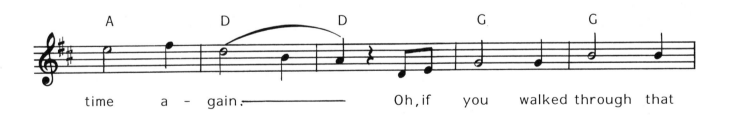

time a - gain.——————— Oh, if you walked through that

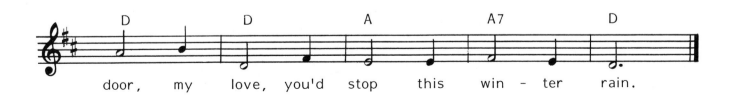

door, my love, you'd stop this win - ter rain.

TAKE IT TO THE LIMIT

Words and Music by RANDY MEISNER,
DON HENLEY and GLEN FREY

BYE BYE LOVE

Words and Music by
FELICE BRYANT and BOUDLEAUX BRYANT

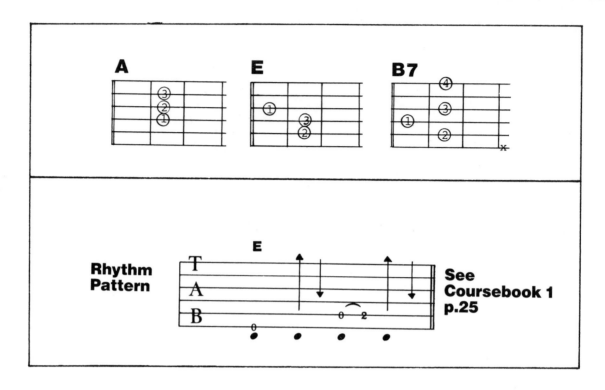

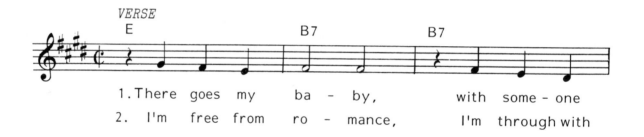

1. There goes my ba - by, with some - one
2. I'm free from ro - mance, I'm through with

new. She sure looks hap - py,
love. I'm through with count - ing

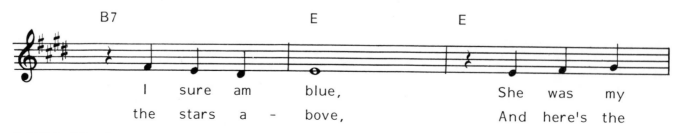

I sure am blue, She was my
the stars a - bove, And here's the

SWEETS FOR MY SWEET

Words and Music by
DOC POMUS and MORT SHUMAN

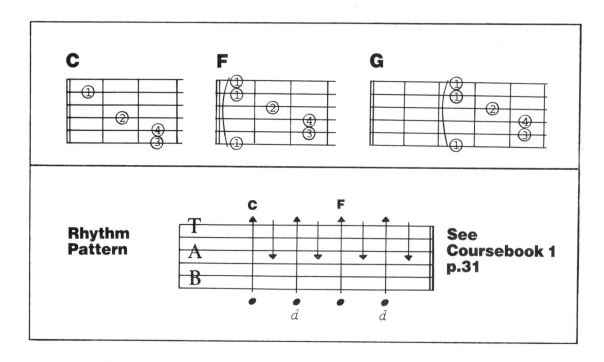

Rhythm Pattern

See Coursebook 1 p.31

VERSE

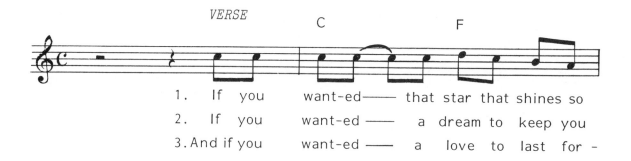

1. If you   want-ed—— that star that shines so
2. If you   want-ed —— a dream to   keep you
3. And if you   want-ed —— a love to   last for -

bright-ly,—— to match the star - dust in your
smil - ing,—— I'd tell the sand - man you were
ev - er,—— darlin' I would send my love your

eyes,—— dar - ling I would chase that bright star
blue,—— and I'd ask him to keep that sand a -
way,—— and my love would not on - ly last for -

© 1961 Brenner Music Inc/Progressive Music Publishing Co Inc/Trio Music Inc, USA
Carlin Music Corp, 14 New Burlington Street, London W1X 2LR

night- ly,—   and try to steal it from the
pil - in',—   un - til your dreams would come
ev - er,—   but for - ev - er and a

CHORUS

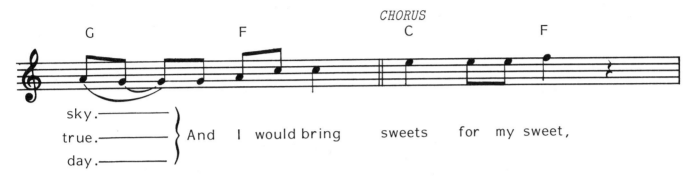

sky.———
true.——— } And I would bring sweets for my sweet,
day.———

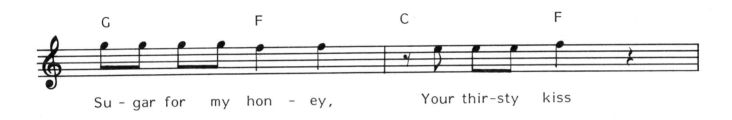

Su - gar for my hon - ey, Your thir-sty kiss

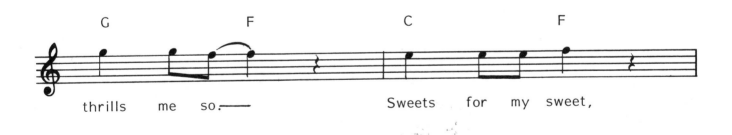

thrills me so.— Sweets for my sweet,

su - gar for my hon- ey, I'll nev-er ev-er— let you go.—

GET OFF MY CLOUD

Words and Music by
MICK JAGGER and KEITH RICHARD

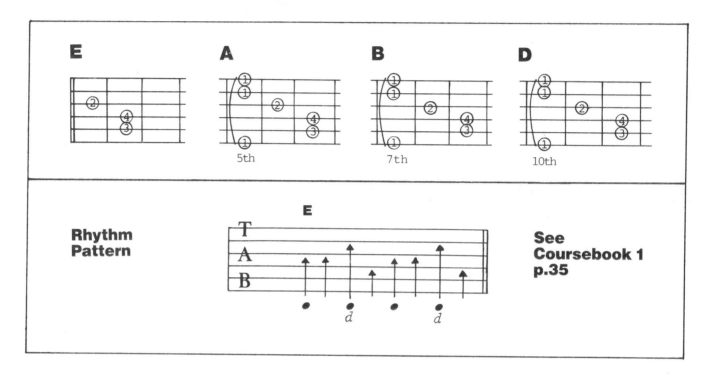

Rhythm Pattern

See Coursebook 1 p.35

VERSE

1. I live in an ap-part-ment on the
2. The tel-e-phone is ring-in' I say
3. I was sick and tired, fed up with this and de-

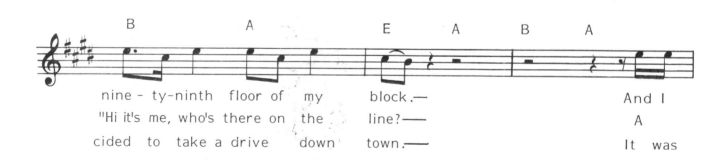

nine-ty-ninth floor of my block.— And I
"Hi it's me, who's there on the line?— A
cided to take a drive down town.— It was

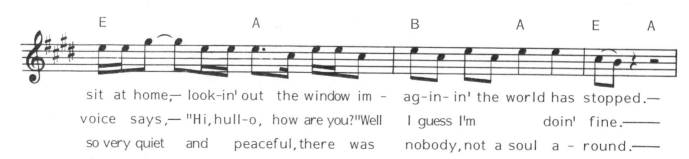

sit at home,— look-in' out the window im-ag-in-in' the world has stopped.—
voice says,— "Hi, hull-o, how are you?" Well I guess I'm doin' fine.——
so very quiet and peaceful, there was nobody, not a soul a-round.——

19

Then in flies— a guy that's all dressed up just like a U-nion—
He says "It's three a.m. and there's too much noise don't you people ev-er want to go to
I laid my— self out, I was so tired and I started to

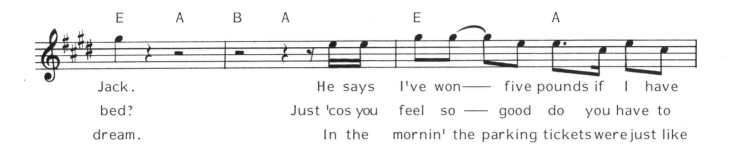

Jack. He says I've won— five pounds if I have
bed? Just 'cos you feel so — good do you have to
dream. In the mornin' the parking tickets were just like

his kind of det - er— gent pack.—
drive me out of— my head?"—
flags stuck on my— wind - screen.—
I said

CHORUS

"Hey, you, get off of my cloud! Hey, you, get

off of my cloud! Hey, you, get off of my cloud!

Don't hang a-round,—'cause two's a crowd,—on my cloud ba-by!"

DON'T STOP

Words and Music
by CHRISTINE McVIE

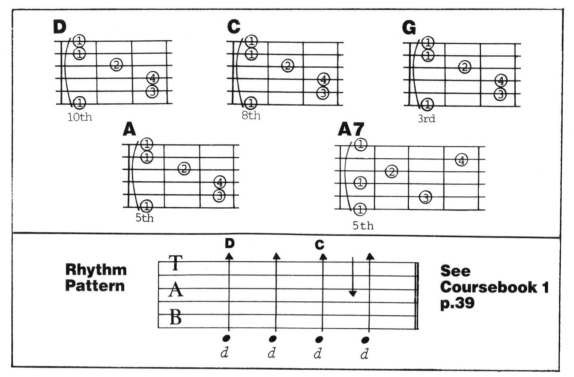

1. If you wake up and don't want to smile,
2. Why not think a - bout time to come;
3. All I want is to see you smile,

if it takes just a lit - tle while.
and not a - bout the things that you've done?
if it takes just a lit - tle while.

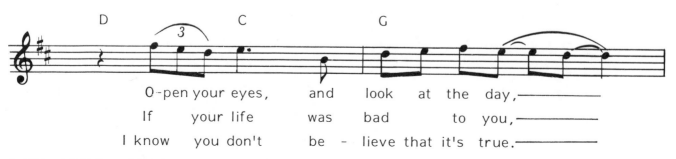

O-pen your eyes, and look at the day,
If your life was bad to you,
I know you don't be - lieve that it's true.

Bright Music Ltd, 34/36 Maddox Street, London W1

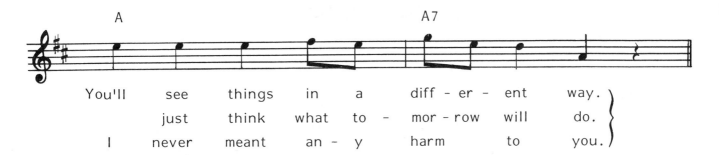

You'll see things in a diff - er - ent way.
just think what to - mor - row will do.
I never meant an - y harm to you.

CHORUS

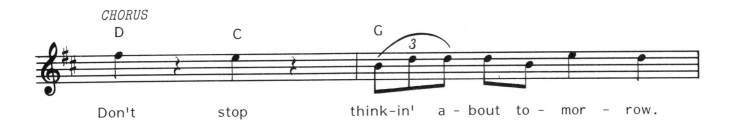

Don't stop think-in' a - bout to - mor - row.

Don't stop, it - 'll soon be here.

It- 'll be bet - ter than be -fore.

Yes- ter -day's gone,— yes - ter-day's gone.—

YOU'RE MY ANGEL

Words and Music
by RUSS SHIPTON

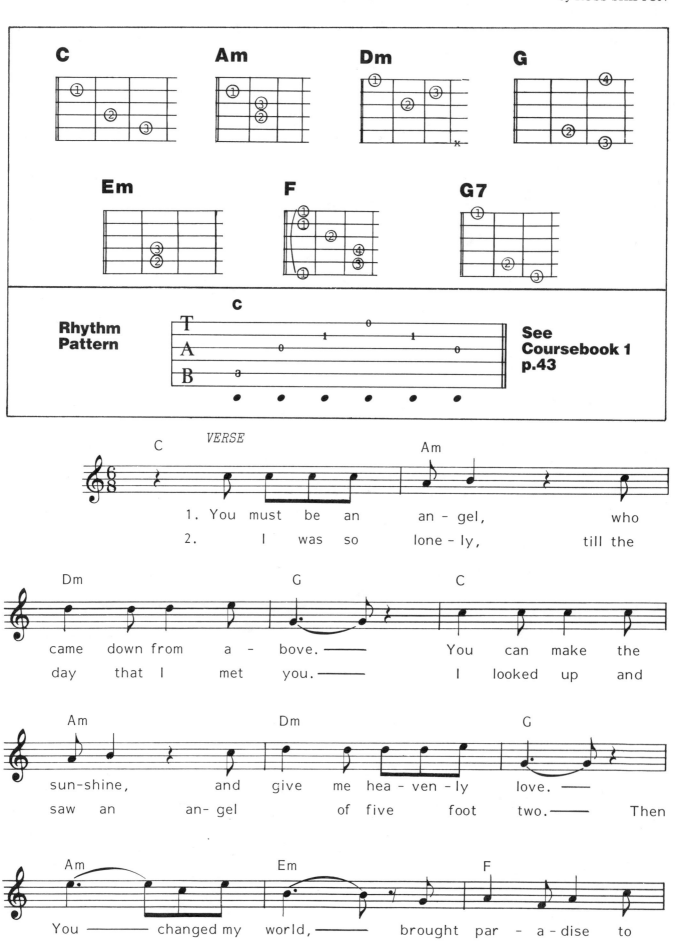

© 1985 Russ Shipton

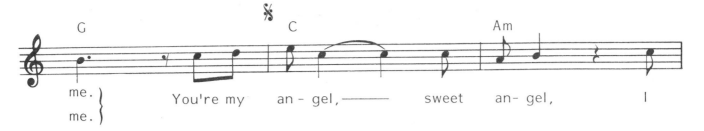

me.
me. You're my an- gel, ——— sweet an- gel, I

pray that you'll be mine, et - er -nal - ly. Oo ee

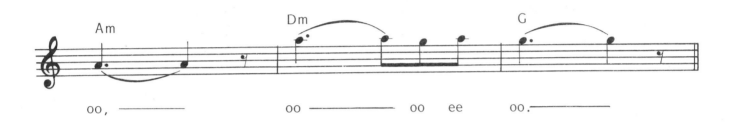

oo, ——— oo ——— oo ee oo.———

MIDDLE SECTION

My an - gel, you know how I love you.

There's no one I'd place a - bove you. Please say you'll

stay with me,— for - ev - er and a day with me, my

PEACEFUL EASY FEELING

Words and Music
by JACK TEMPCHIN

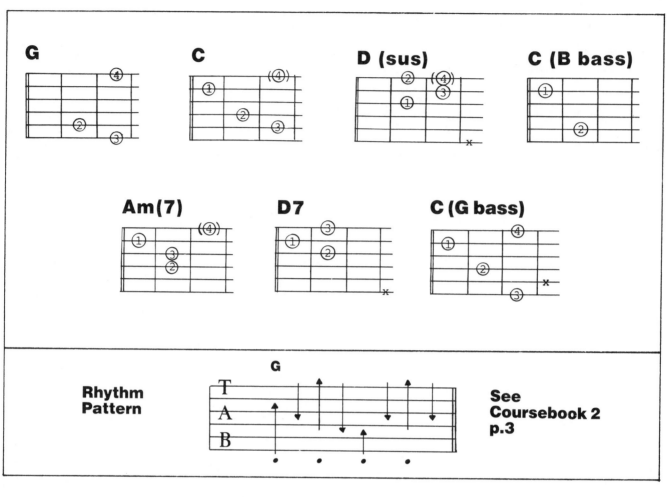

I wan - na sleep with you— in the des - ert— to -
Ah, but she can't take— you an - y -
But this voice keeps whis-per - ing— in my oth - er

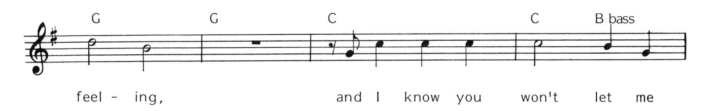

night, with a bill - ion stars all— a -
way, you don't alread - y know how— to
ear. Tells me I may nev - er see you— a -

CHORUS

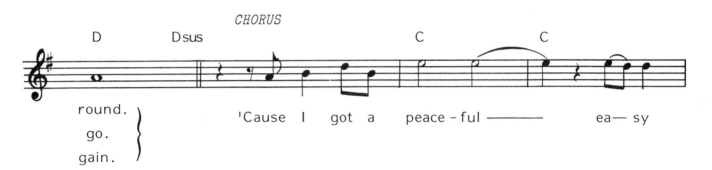

round. ⎫
go. ⎬ 'Cause I got a peace - ful ——— ea— sy
gain. ⎭

feel - ing, and I know you won't let me

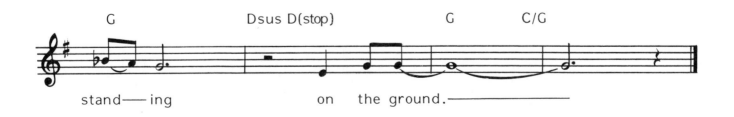

down,———— 'cause I'm al ———— read-y

stand—ing on the ground.————

ONLY SIXTEEN

Words and Music
by BARBARA CAMPBELL

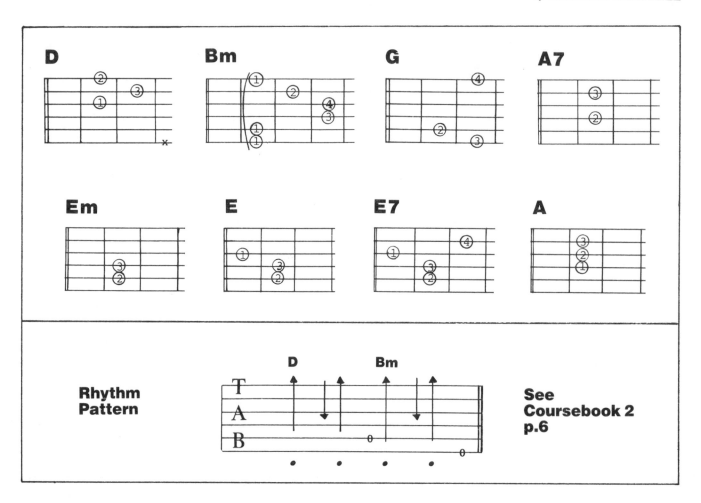

Rhythm Pattern

See Coursebook 2 p.6

1. She was on - ly six - teen,—
2. laugh and we'd sing,— and
3. on - ly six - teen,—

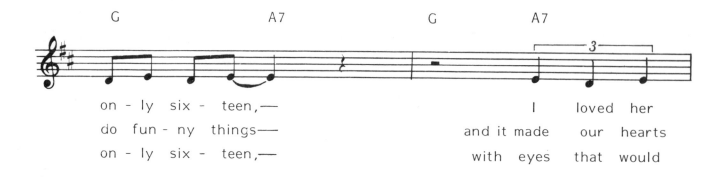

on - ly six - teen,— I loved her
do fun - ny things— and it made our hearts
on - ly six - teen,— with eyes that would

so,
glow,
glow,

but she was too young to

fall in love —— and I —— was too young —— to

MIDDLE SECTION

know. 2.We'd Why did I give my

heart so fast? —— It nev-er will hap-pen— a-

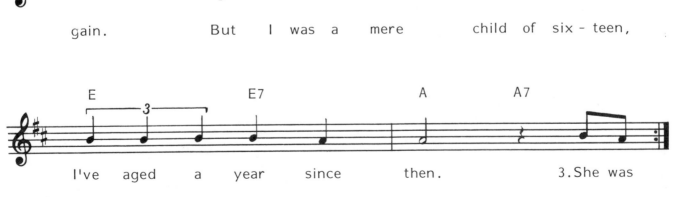

gain. But I was a mere child of six-teen,

I've aged a year since then. 3.She was

ROCKIN' ALL OVER THE WORLD

Words and Music
by JOHN FOGERTY

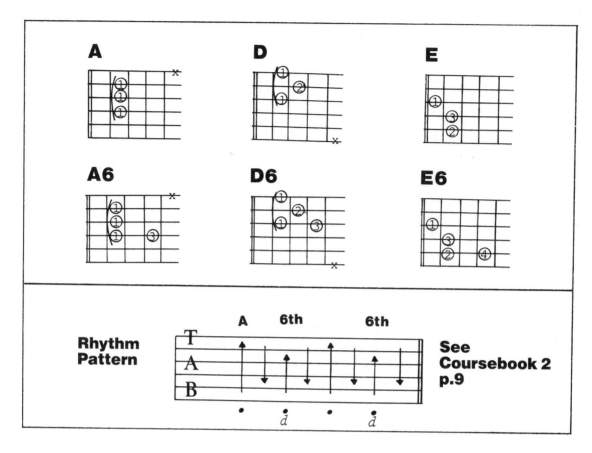

VERSES 1, 2 & 4

1. Well here we are and here we are and
2. Well gid-dy up and gid-dy up and
4. Gonna tell your mom — ma what you're

here we—— go, On and on, —— and we're
get a—— way, We're go-in' cra-y and we're
gon-na—— do, Come on a-round,—— get your

hit-tin' the road.——
go-in' to-day.—— } Here we go,————
danc-in'—— shoes.——

© 1976 Primeval Ltd
Intersong Music Ltd, London W1Y 3FA

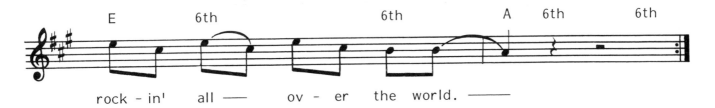

rock - in' all —— ov - er the world. ——

VERSE 3

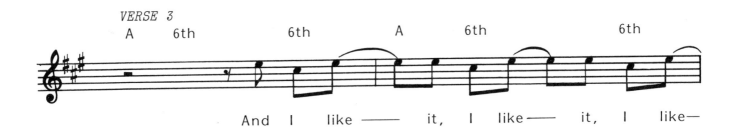

And I like —— it, I like—— it, I like—

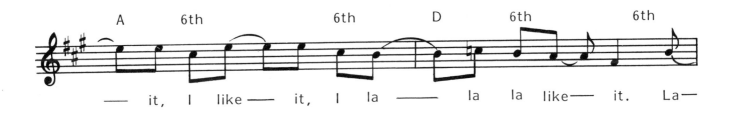

—— it, I like —— it, I la —— la la like— it. La—

—— la la la. —— Here we go, ————————

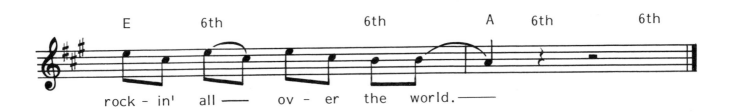

rock - in' all — ov - er the world.——

ROLL OVER BEETHOVEN

Words and Music
by CHUCK BERRY

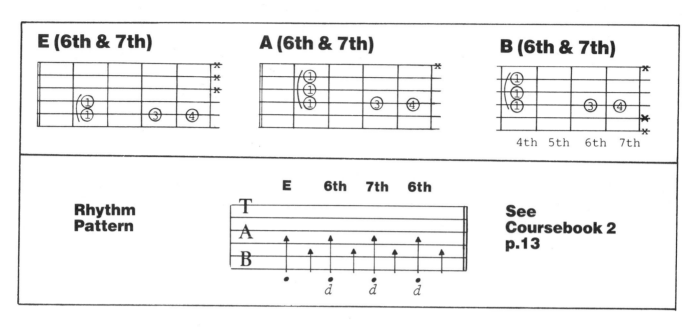

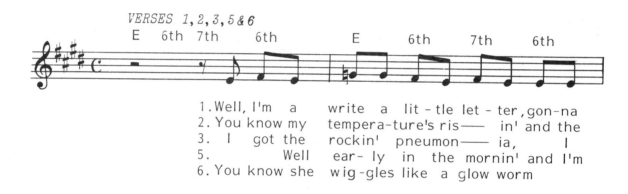

E 6th 7th 6th   B 6th 7th 6th

1.   Roll   ov - er Beet- hov —— en,   got to
2.   Roll   ov - er Beet- hov —— en,   and
3.   Roll   ov - er Beet- hov —— en,   they're
5. lose.   Roll   ov - er Beet- hov —— en,   and
6.   Long as she's got a dime,   the

A 6th 7th 6th   E 6th 7th 6th

1. hear it a - gain —— to - day. ——
2. tell Tchaikov —— sky the news. ——
3. rock- in' in two   by two. ——
5. tell Tchaikov —— sky the news. ——
6. mu - sic won't ev —— er stop. ——

VERSE 4

E 6th 7th 6th   E 6th 7th 6th   E 6th 7th 6th

Well, if you feel you like it,   go get your lov-er, then

E 6th 7th 6th   E 6th 7th 6th

reel and rock it,   roll —— it ov - er, then

A 6th 7th 6th   A 6th 7th 6th

move on up just a   tri — fle fur- ther, then

E 6th 7th 6th   E 6th 7th 6th

reel and rock with   one —— an- oth - er. Roll

B 6th 7th 6th   A 6th 7th 6th   E 6th 7th 6th

ov - er Beet- ho — ven — Dig these rhy- thm and blues. ——

JAILHOUSE ROCK

Words and Music by
JERRY LEIBER and MIKE STOLLER

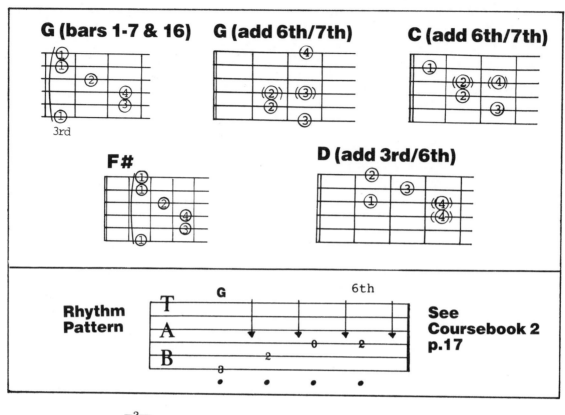

1. – gan   to swing.—   You   should-'ve heard those knocked out
2. crash, boom,   bang.   The   whole   rhy- thm section was the
3. com – pa – ny.—   Come   on and do the jail – house
4. be   no   square.   If you can't   find a partner, use a
5. said   "Nix,   nix.   I   wan – na stick a-round a while and

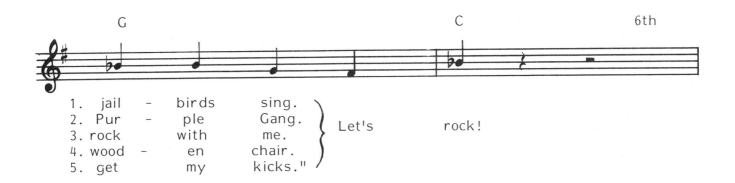

1. jail   – birds   sing.
2. Pur – ple   Gang.
3. rock   with   me.   Let's   rock!
4. wood – en   chair.
5. get   my   kicks."

Let's   rock!   Eve – ry

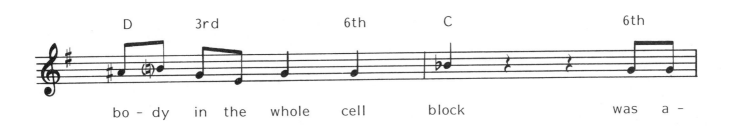

bo – dy in the whole cell   block   was a –

danc – ing   to   the   jail – house   rock!   (4. The)

THAT'LL BE THE DAY

Words and Music by BUDDY HOLLY,
NORMAN PETTY and JERRY ALLISON

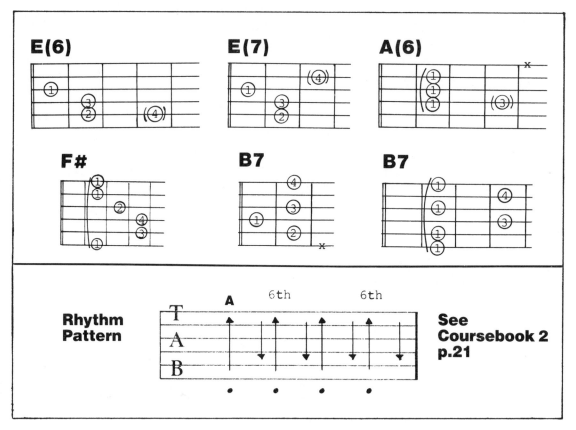

Rhythm Pattern

See Coursebook 2 p.21

1.Well, you give me all your lov-in' and your

2. When Cu-pid shot his dart,

tur — tle dov-in'— all your hugs and kiss-es an' your

he shot it at your heart. So if we ev-er part and

mon-ey too.— Well, you know you love me, ba-by,

I leave you, you say you told me an' you

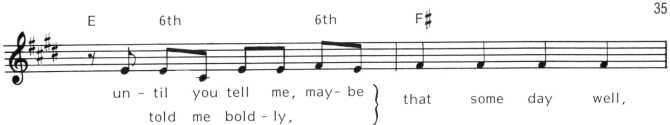

E　　　　6th　　　　　　　6th　　　F#

un‐til　you tell　me, may‐be
told　me　bold‐ly,
that　　some　day　well,

CHORUS

B7(pos 2)　　　　　　　　　　　A　　　6th　　　　6th

I'll　be　through. Well,——　　that‐'ll　be　the day,　　when

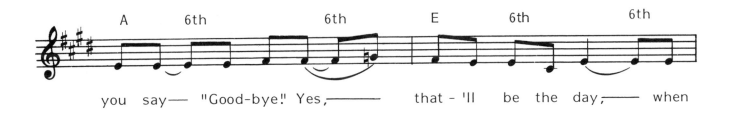

A　　6th　　　　　6th　　　　E　　6th　　　　6th

you　say——　"Good‐bye!" Yes,——　that‐'ll　be　the day;——　when

E　　　　　E7　　　　　　A　　　6th　　　　6th

you　make——　me cry. Oh——　you　say you're gon‐na leave,——　you

E　　6th　　6th　E(stop)　　　　　E B7　　E

know it's　a lie,——'cause that‐'ll be the day————— when I die.——

EVERY BREATH YOU TAKE

Words and Music
by STING

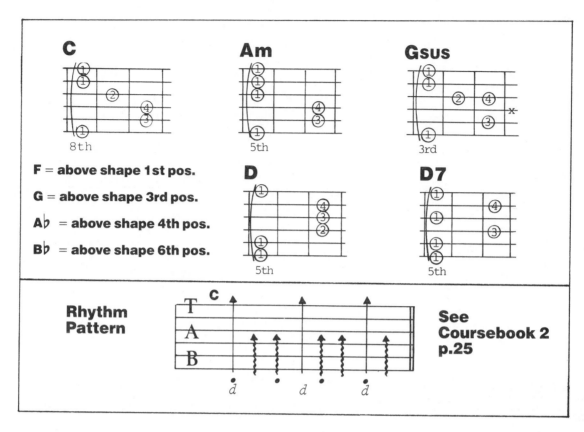

F = above shape 1st pos.

G = above shape 3rd pos.

Ab = above shape 4th pos.

Bb = above shape 6th pos.

Rhythm Pattern

See Coursebook 2 p.25

VERSE

C   C

1. Ev-'ry breath you— take,   and ev-'ry move you—
2. Ev-'ry move you— make,   and ev-'ry vow you—

Am   Am   F

make;   ev-'ry bond you   break; ev-'ry step you
break;   ev-'ry smile you   fake; ev-'ry claim you

Gsus   Am   Am

take; I'll be watching you. }
stake; I'll be watching you. }

Ev-'ry sin - gle——

C   C   Am

day,   and ev-'ry word you— say;

© 1983 Virgin Music (Publishers) Ltd

I'M NOT IN LOVE

Words and Music by
ERIC STEWART and GRAHAM GOULDMAN

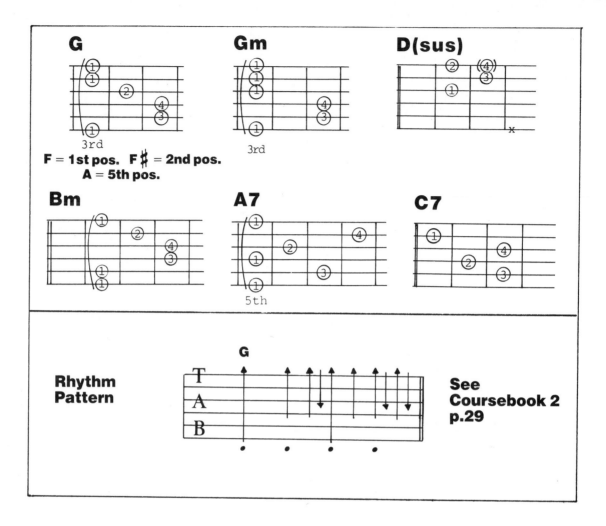

F = 1st pos. F♯ = 2nd pos.
A = 5th pos.

Rhythm Pattern

See Coursebook 2 p.29

VERSE

G	Gm

1. I'm not in love, —— so don't for-get it, ——
2. I like to see you, — but then a-gain, ——
3. I keep your pic-ture— up - on the wall, ——

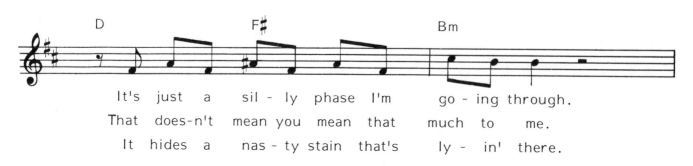

D   F♯   Bm

It's just a sil - ly phase I'm go - ing through.
That does-n't mean you mean that much to me.
It hides a nas - ty stain that's ly - in' there.

And just be - cause ———— I call you up ————
So if I call you,— don't make a fuss,————
So don't you ask me, — to give it back,————

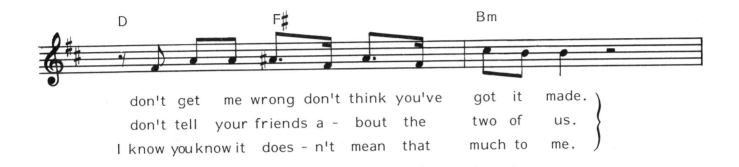

don't get me wrong don't think you've got it made.
don't tell your friends a - bout the two of us.
I know you know it does - n't mean that much to me.

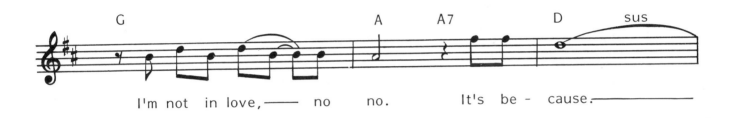

I'm not in love, ——— no no. It's be - cause.————

MIDDLE SECTION

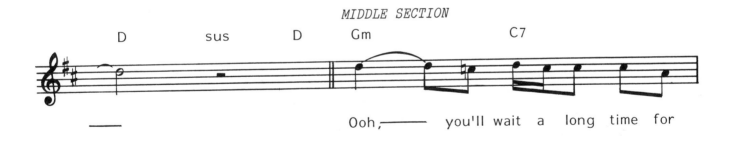

——— Ooh,——— you'll wait a long time for

me.——— Ooh,——— you'll wait a long time.

RED RED WINE

Words and Music
by NEIL DIAMOND

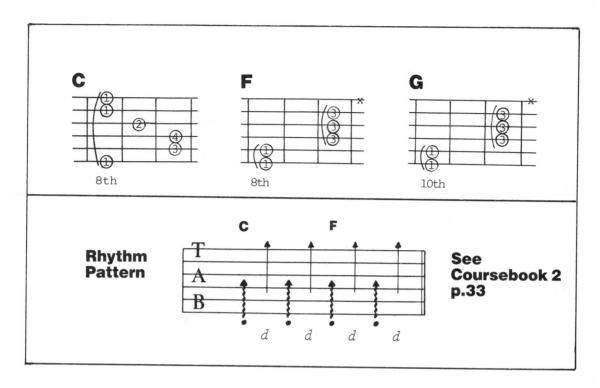

Rhythm Pattern

See Coursebook 2 p.33

1. Red, red wine,———— goes to my
2. Red, red wine,———— it's up to

head.———— Makes me for - get that I
you.———— All I can do I've done,

still need her so.—— Memo-ries won't go.——
Memo-ries won't go.——

I'd have sworn, that with time,——

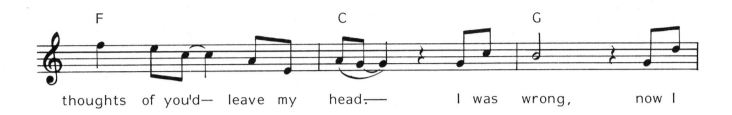

thoughts of you'd— leave my head.— I was wrong, now I

find just one thing makes me for - get. Red, red

wine,——————— stay close to me.———————

Don't let me be a-lone.— It's tear-in' a -

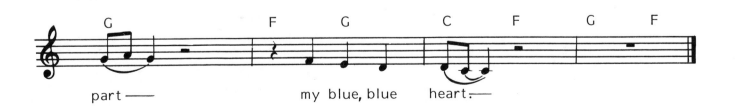

part —— my blue, blue heart.—

ALWAYS WANT YOU THERE

Words and Music
by RUSS SHIPTON

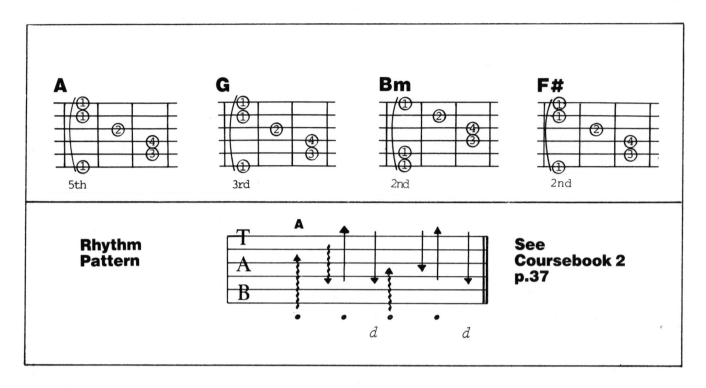

Rhythm Pattern

See Coursebook 2 p.37

Want you to know —— how much I love —

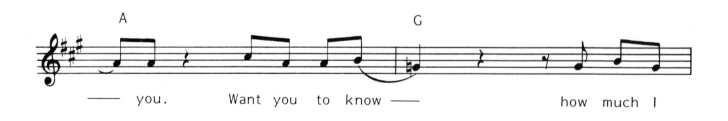

—— you. Want you to know —— how much I

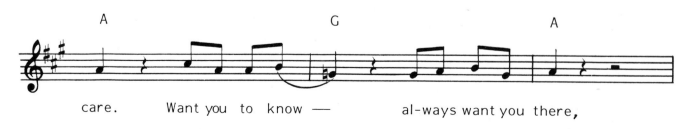

care. Want you to know — al-ways want you there,

al-ways want you there.

VERSE

1. Oh babe, the num-ber of times— I've
2. May-be I've done some run-nin' a-round— but

let you down— it's a crime— I know.
in my heart, what I've found I know.

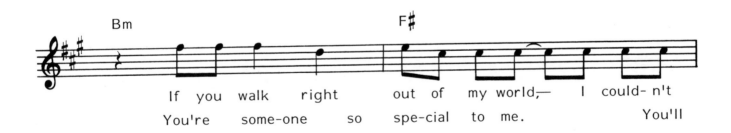

If you walk right out of my world,— I could-n't
You're some-one so spe-cial to me. You'll

blame you girl,— but please don't go.
al-ways be,— so please don't go.

ONLY TIME WILL TELL

Words and Music
by RUSS SHIPTON

Rhythm Pattern See Coursebook 2 p.42

CHORUS

C	C	F

Time will tell if you're right or

C	C	C

wrong. You say that I'll be leav-ing you be-

G	G7	C

fore too — long. I say I'll be

C	F	C

with you till there is ice in hell.

Still you don't be - lieve me, and on- ly time will tell.

VERSE

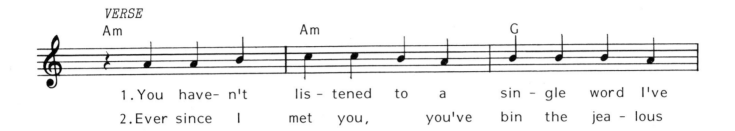

1. You have- n't lis - tened to a sin - gle word I've
2. Ever since I met you, you've bin the jea - lous

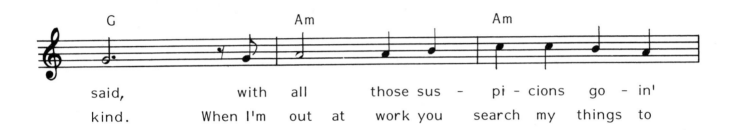

said, with all those sus - pi - cions go - in'
kind. When I'm out at work you search my things to

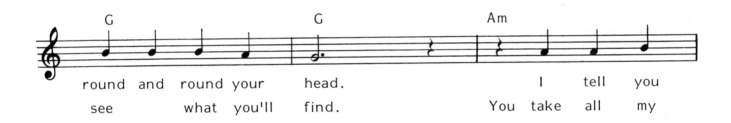

round and round your head. I tell you
see what you'll find. You take all my

black ain't white and night can't be day, but you'd
let - ters and you hold them to the light. You won - der

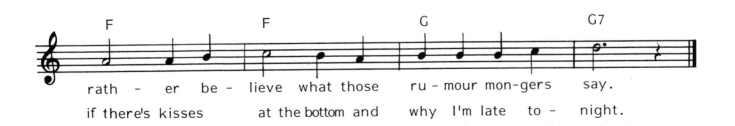

rath - er be - lieve what those ru - mour mon-gers say.
if there's kisses at the bottom and why I'm late to - night.

WHERE THE ACTION IS

Words and Music
by RUSS SHIPTON

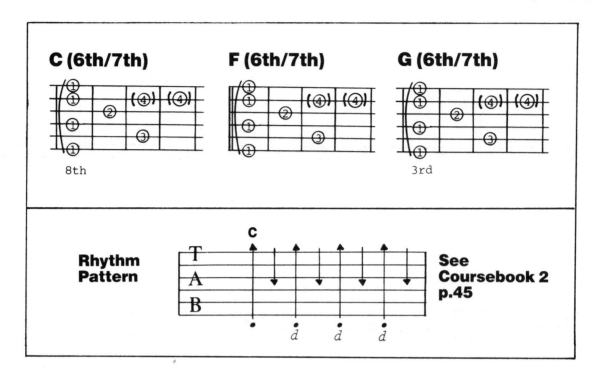

C (6th/7th) 8th   **F (6th/7th)**   **G (6th/7th)** 3rd

Rhythm Pattern   See Coursebook 2 p.45

C   6th   7th   6th   C   6th   7th   6th

1. Noth-in's go-in' on here.— What kind-a place— d'ya call
2. Some-times I feel like I'm a moth—er-less
3. jump in my Chev—ro-let, let's give this hick—town a

C 6th 7th 6th   C 6th C7   F   6th   7th   6th

this?   Quiet-er than a grave-yard,— a
child.   Got a tel-e-phone line ——— with-
miss.   Find some-where to boo-gie,

F   6th   7th   6th   C 6th 7th 6th   C 6th 7th 6th

so - da with- out—— an - y fizz.
out an - y num—— bers to dial.
that's a lit - tle hot-ter than this.

         Let's

Want some sat - is - fact-ion, — go-in' where the act-ion — is! —
Want some sat - is - fact-ion, go-in' where the re - act — ion is wild! —
get some sat - is - fact-ion, and head to where the act - ion — is! —

VERSE 4

Go-in' where the act-ion — is. —

3. Come on and

We're go - in' where the act - ion — is. —

Yes, we're go - in' where the act-ion — is. —

Go - in' where the act-ion — is. — Want some sat-is-faction, so we're

go - in' where the act - ion — is! ——

LEAD ME ON

Music by
RUSS SHIPTON

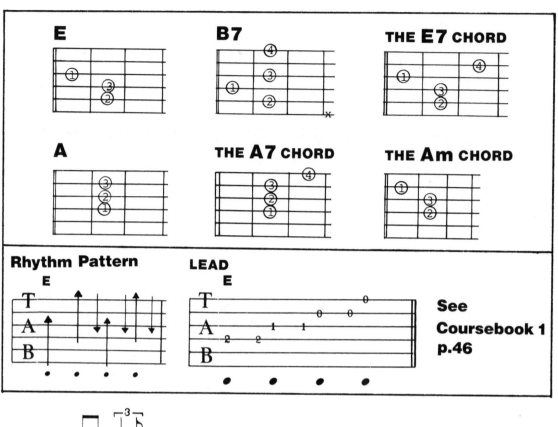

Rhythm Pattern   **LEAD**   See Coursebook 1 p.46

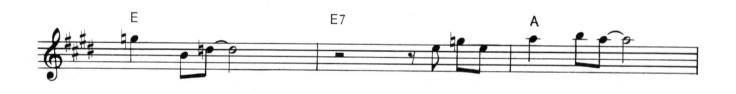

RUSS SHIPTON'S Rock & Pop Guitar Songbook 2

Contents

Note: The songs in this book are taken from "Russ Shiptons Rock & Pop Guitar" Coursebooks 3 + 4. The Coursebooks and matching cassettes include the analysis and demonstration of chords, rhythm patterns and techniques needed to play the accompaniments effectively (see back cover)

First Published 1986
© International Music Publications

Exclusive Distributors
International Music Publications
Southend Road, Woodford Green,
Essex IG8 8HN, England.

Printed in England by JB Offset (Marks Tey) Limited
Marks Tey, Essex.

PRETTY VACANT

Words and Music by JOHNNY ROTTEN,
PAUL COOK, STEVEN JONES and GLEN MATLOCK

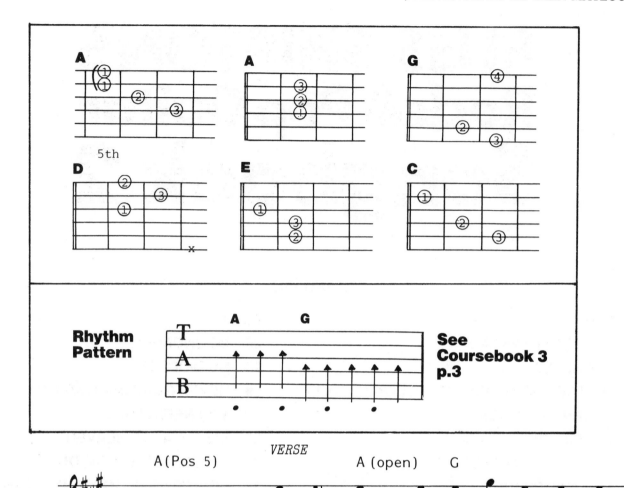

Rhythm Pattern

See Coursebook 3 p.3

VERSE

A(Pos 5)   A (open)   G

1. There's   no   point in ask- in' you'll get
2.   ask us to at - tend   'cos we're

D   A   G   E

no re-ply.—   I just re - mem-ber, I don't de-cide.—   I
not all there.— Oh don't pre - tend   'cos I don't care.— I

A   G   D   A   G

got no rea-son, it's all too much.— You'll al - ways find us—
don't believe illusions, 'cos too much is real.— So stop your cheap comment,—

out to lunch. —   Oh
'cos we know what we feel. —   Oh

CHORUS

we're so pret-ty, —   oh so pret-ty, —   a -

va - cant. —   oh we're so pret-ty, —   oh so pret-ty, —

a - va - cant. — (2.Don't) We're so pret-ty, —

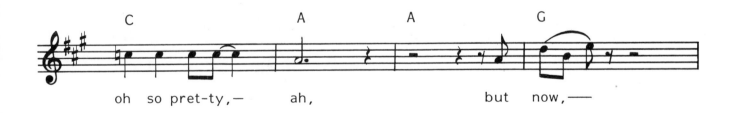

oh so pret-ty, —   ah,   but now, —

and we don't— care! —————————————

HELLO

Words and Music
by LIONEL RICHIE

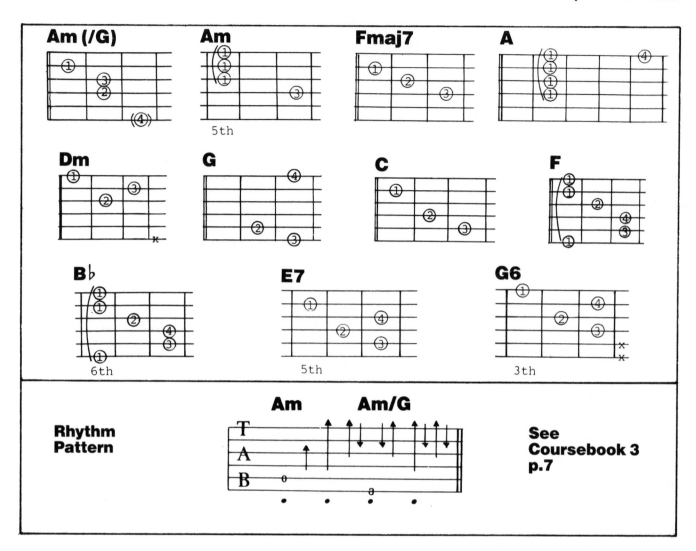

1. I've been a-lone with you in-side my
2. I long to see the sun-light in your

mind,—— and in my dreams I've kissed your lips
hair,—— and tell you time and time a-gain

a thou-sand times. I some-times see you pass out-side my
how much I care. Some-times I feel my heart will ov-er-

door.— Hell - o, is it me you're look-ing for? I can
flow.— Hell - o, I've just got to let you know. 'cos I

see it in your eyes, I can see it in your smile. You're
won-der where you are, and I won-der what you do, Are you

all I've ev - er want-ed, and my arms are o - pen wide, 'Cos you
some-where feel-ing lone-ly, or is some - one lov- ing you, Tell me

know just what to say and you know just what to do,— and I
how to win your heart, for I have-n't got a clue,— but

want to tell you so much, I love you.
let me start by say - ing "I love you."

IT'S ONLY ROCK & ROLL (BUT I LIKE IT)

Words and Music by
MICK JAGGER and KEITH RICHARDS

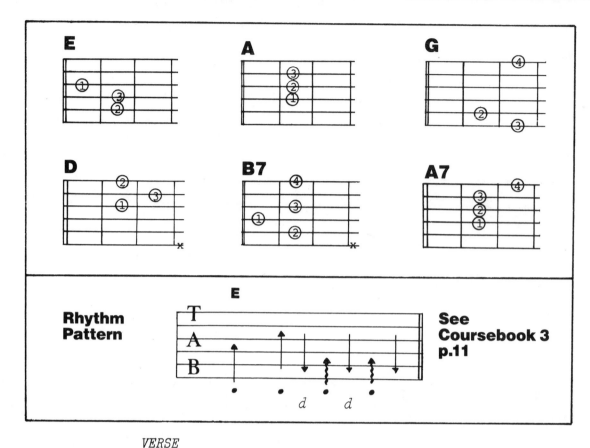

Rhythm Pattern

See Coursebook 3 p.11

VERSE

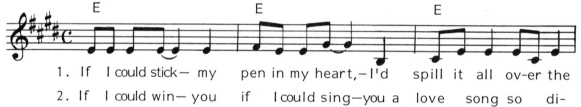

1. If I could stick— my pen in my heart,—I'd spill it all ov-er the
2. If I could win— you if I could sing—you a love song so di-
3. If I could stick— a knife in my heart;— su-i- cide right on the
4. If I could dig—down deep in my heart,— feel-ings would flood on the

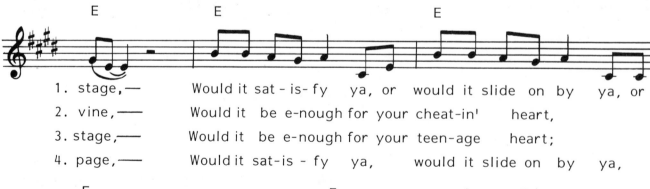

1. stage,— Would it sat-is-fy ya, or would it slide on by ya, or
2. vine,— Would it be e-nough for your cheat-in' heart,
3. stage,— Would it be e-nough for your teen-age heart;
4. page,— Would it sat-is-fy ya, would it slide on by ya,

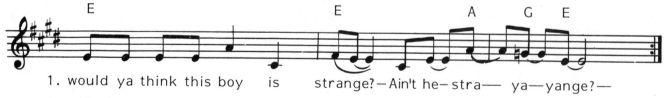

1. would ya think this boy is strange?—Ain't he-stra— ya—yange?—
2. if I broke down and cried,— if I— cri— yi— yied?—
3. would it help to ease the pain,— ease the—bra— ya —yain?—
4. would you think the boy's in - sane; he's in— sa — ya— yane?—

BROWN SUGAR

Words and Music by
MICK JAGGER and KEITH RICHARDS

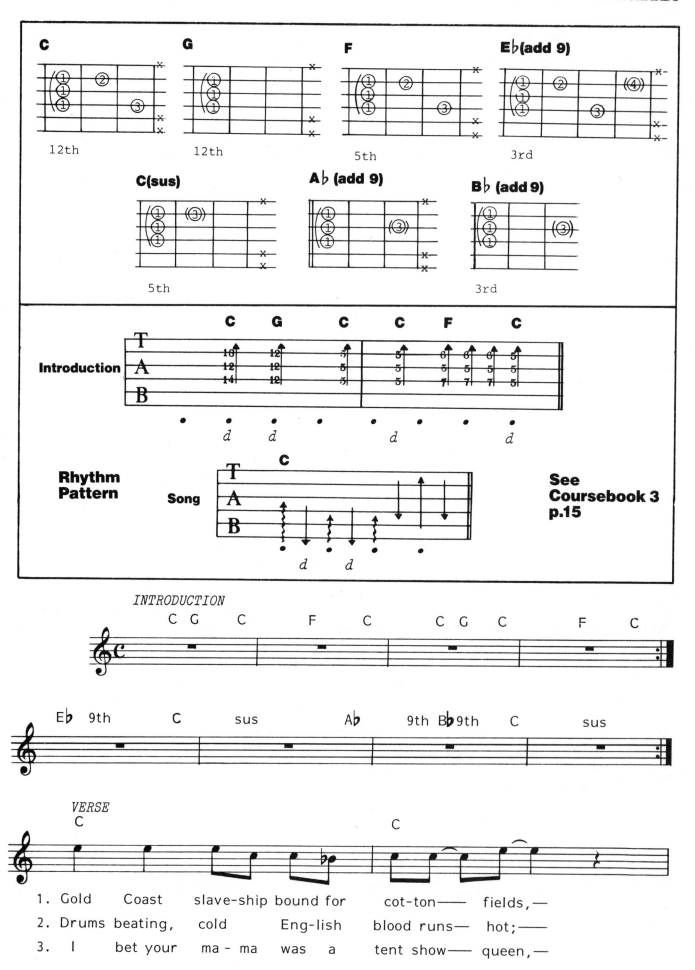

sold in a mar-ket down in New Or— leans.—
lady of the house wonderin' where it's gon-na stop.—
and all her girl — friends were sweet six— teen.——

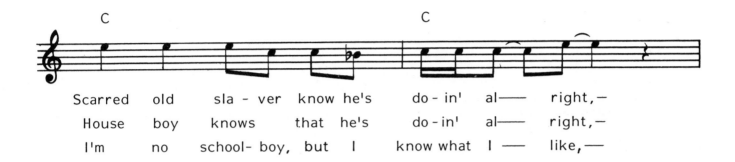

Scarred old sla - ver know he's do - in' al—— right,—
House boy knows that he's do - in' al—— right,—
I'm no school- boy, but I know what I — like,—

CHORUS

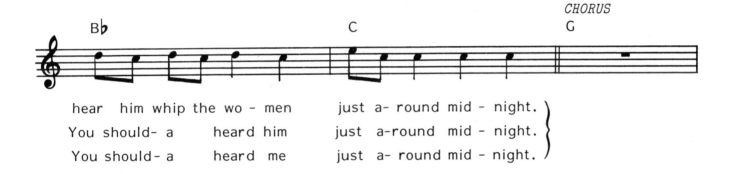

hear him whip the wo - men just a- round mid - night.
You should- a heard him just a-round mid - night.
You should- a heard me just a- round mid - night.

Brown Su-gar,— how come ya taste so good? ———

Brown Su-gar,— just like a young girl—should. ———

PINBALL WIZARD

Words and Music
by PETE TOWNSHEND

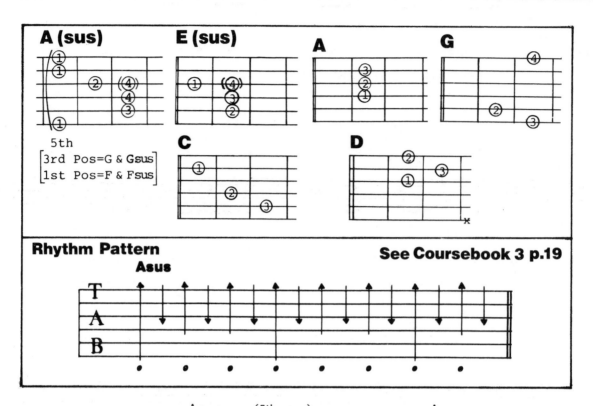

Rhythm Pattern **See Coursebook 3 p.19**

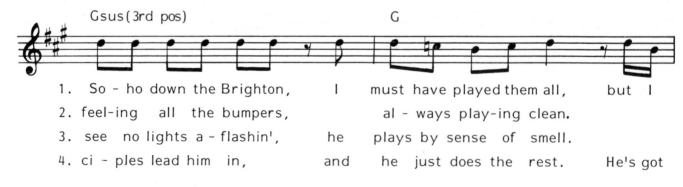

1. Ev-er since I was a young boy, I've played the sil-ver ball. From
2. stands like a sta-tue, becomes part of the ma-chine,
3. Ain't got no dis-tractions, can't hear no buzzers and bells. Don't
4. Ev-en on my favourite ta-ble, he can beat my best. His dis-

1. So - ho down the Brighton, I must have played them all, but I
2. feel-ing all the bumpers, al - ways play-ing clean.
3. see no lights a - flashin', he plays by sense of smell.
4. ci - ples lead him in, and he just does the rest. He's got

1. ain't seen noth-in' like him, in an-y a-mus-ment hall.
2. Plays by in - tu - i - tion the di - git coun- ters fall. } That
3. Al - ways gets a re-play, nev - er tilts at all.
4. cra - zy, flip - pin' fin-gers, nev - er seen him fall.

deaf, dumb and blind kid——— sure plays a mean pin -

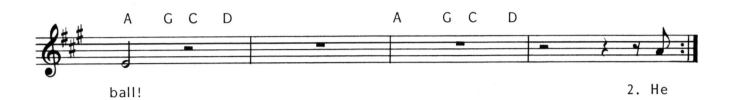

ball! 2. He

MIDDLE SECTION

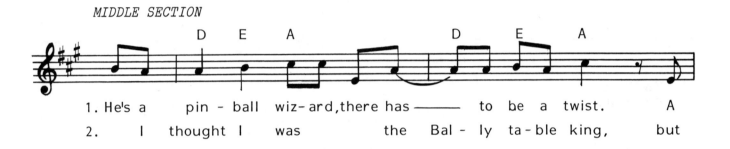

1. He's a pin - ball wiz-ard, there has ——— to be a twist. A
2. I thought I was the Bal - ly ta-ble king, but

pin - ball wiz - ard, got such a sup - ple
I've just hand- ed my pin - ball crown to

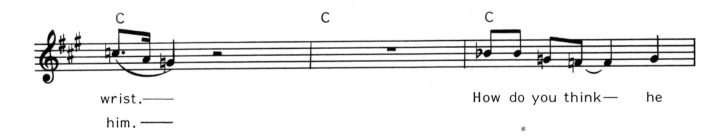

wrist.——— How do you think— he
him. ———

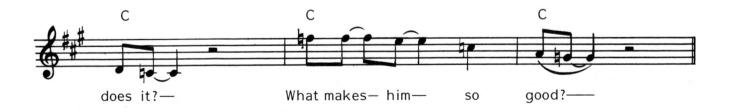

does it?— What makes— him— so good?——

LISTEN TO THE MUSIC

Words and Music
by TOM JOHNSTON

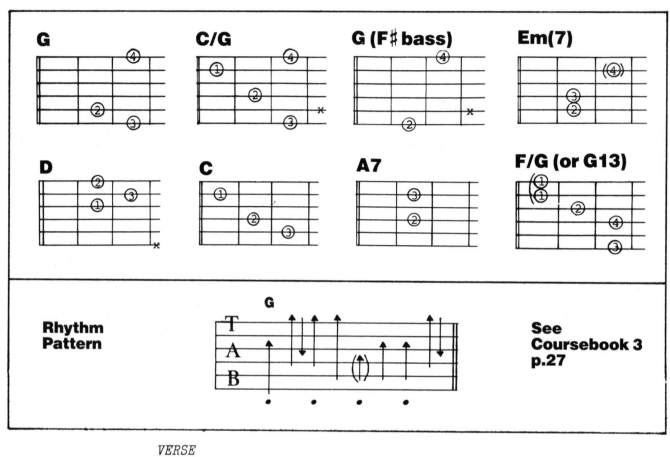

Rhythm Pattern

See Coursebook 3 p.27

VERSE

1. Don't you feel it grow-in'—— day by— day?—
2. What the peo-ple need —— is a way to make 'em smile. It
3. Well I know you bet-ter,—— eve-ry-thing I say.
4. If I'm feel-in' good to you, and you're feel-in good to me,

1. Peo-ple, get-tin' rea-dy for the news. Some are
2. ain't so hard to do if you know how. Gotta getta
3. Meet me in the country for a day. We'll be
4. there ain't nothin' we can't do or say. Feel-in'

1. hap——py,— some are sad.———————— oh——
2. mess——age—— get in on through.———————— oh——
3. hap——py,— and we'll dance.———————— Oh——
4. good,——— feel-in' fine.———————— Oh——

1. — we got-ta let the mu - sic play.—
2.— mom-ma's goin' to after a
3. — we're gon-na dance our blues a - way.— 4. And
4.— ba - by let the mu - sic

2. while } Oh— oh, lis-ten to the mus-ic, Oh— oh, lis-ten to the
4. play }

mu-sic, Oh— oh, lis-ten to the mu-sic, all the time.—

MIDDLE SECTION

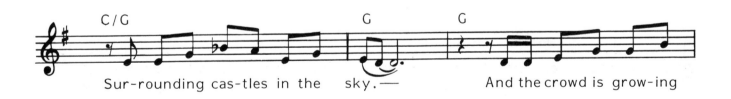

— Like a la - zy, flow-ing riv-er.—

Sur-rounding cas-tles in the sky.— And the crowd is grow-ing

big-ger,— lis-tening for the hap-py sounds,-and I got to let—them fly. Oh—

JIVE TALKIN'

Words and Music by
BARRY, ROBIN and MAURICE GIBB

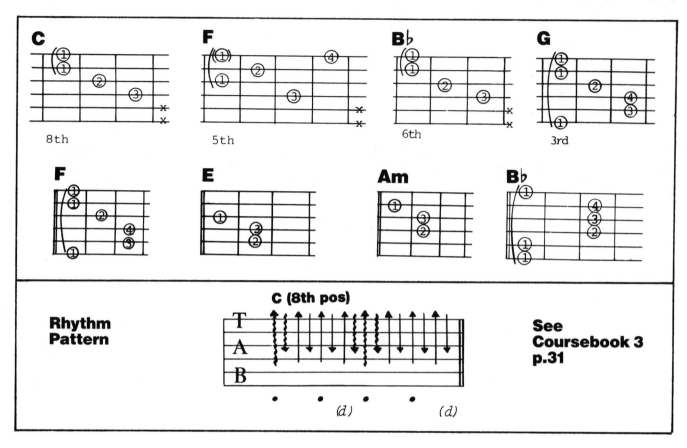

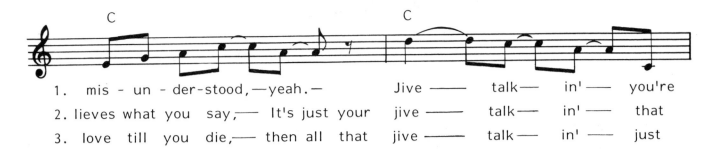

C C

1. mis - un - der-stood,—yeah.— Jive ——— talk— in' ——— you're
2. lieves what you say,—— It's just your jive ——— talk— in' ——— that
3. love till you die,—— then all that jive ——— talk— in' ——— just

MIDDLE SECTION

B♭ .... C .... G .... F

1. real - ly no good. —
2. gets in the way.——
3. gets in your eye. ——

1. Oh, my child,—
2. Oh, my love,—

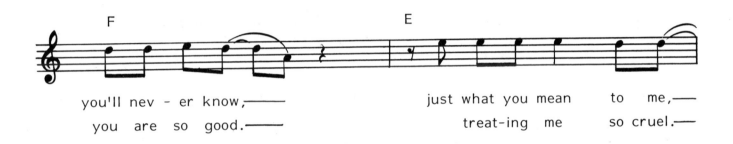

F .... E

you'll nev - er know,—— just what you mean to me,—
you are so good.—— treat-ing me so cruel.—

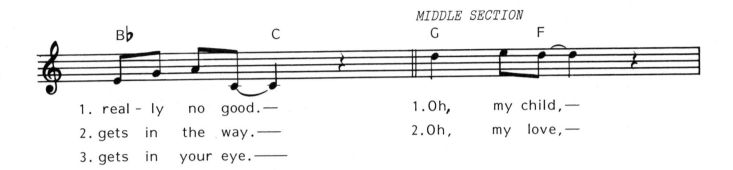

Am .... G ... F .... F

Oh, my child,— you got so much.—
There you go,— with your fan —— cy lies,—

C .... B♭ .... F .... G

You're gon - na take a - way— my en - er - gy, with all your
leav - in' me look-ing like— a dumb - struck fool, with all your

LE FREAK

Words and Music by
NILE RODGERS and BERNARD EDWARDS

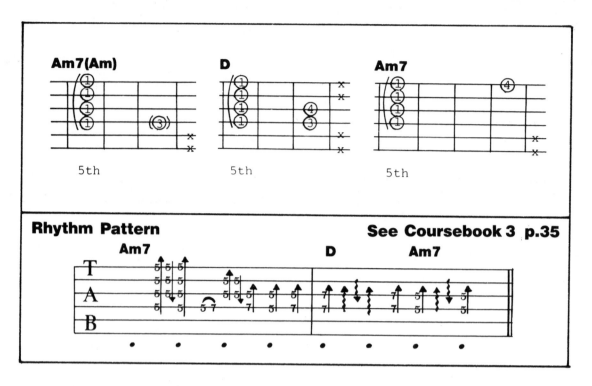

Rhythm Pattern   **See Coursebook 3 p.35**

VERSE

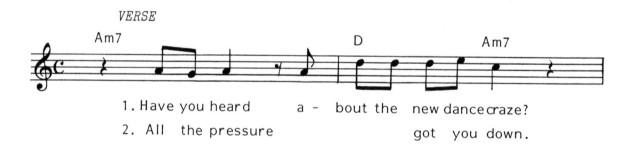

1. Have you heard   a - bout the   new dance craze?
2. All   the pressure   got   you down.

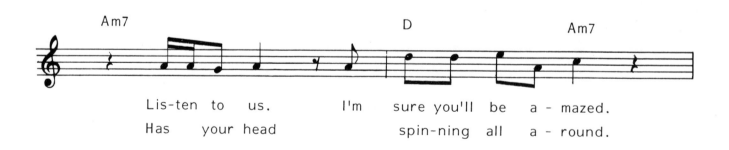

Lis-ten to   us.   I'm   sure you'll be   a - mazed.
Has   your head   spin-ning all   a - round.

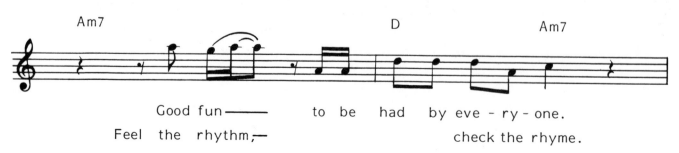

Good fun —— to be   had   by eve - ry - one.
Feel   the rhythm, —   check the rhyme.

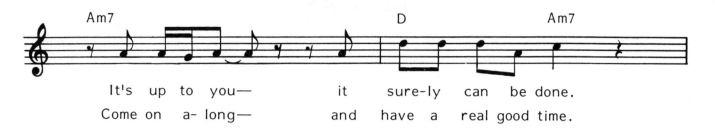

It's up to you— it sure-ly can be done.
Come on a- long— and have a real good time.

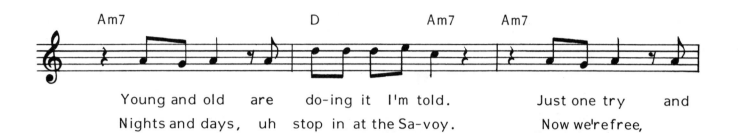

Young and old are do-ing it I'm told. Just one try and
Nights and days, uh stop in at the Sa-voy. Now we're free,

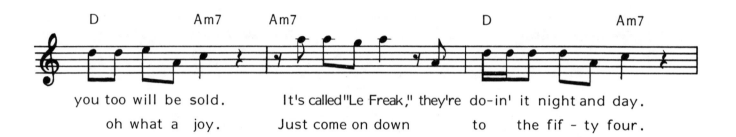

you too will be sold. It's called "Le Freak," they're do-in' it night and day.
oh what a joy. Just come on down to the fif - ty four.

Al - low us, we'll show you the way. Ah —— freak
Find your spot out on the floor.

out! Le Freak, c'est chic. Freak out! Now

BREAK

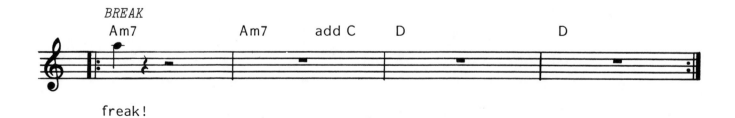

freak!

THE CLOAK

Words and Music
by RUSS SHIPTON

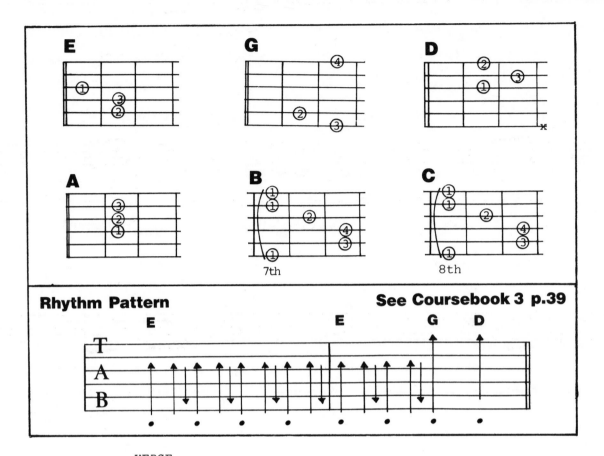

Rhythm Pattern **See Coursebook 3 p.39**

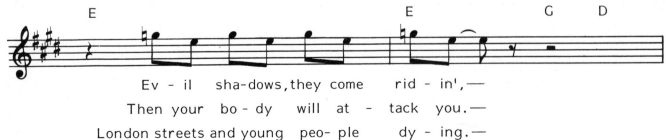

VERSE

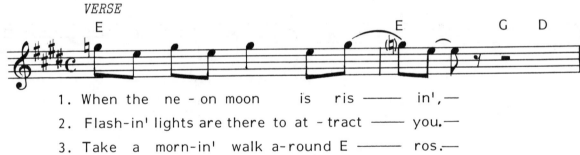

1. When the ne - on moon   is ris —— in', —
2. Flash-in' lights are there to at - tract —— you. —
3. Take a morn-in' walk a-round E —— ros. —

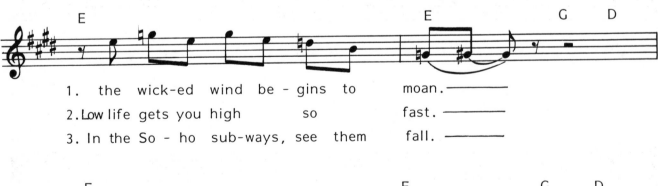

1. the wick-ed wind be - gins to   moan. ——
2. Low life gets you high   so   fast. ——
3. In the So - ho sub-ways, see them   fall. ——

Ev - il sha-dows, they come   rid - in', —
Then your bo - dy   will at - tack you. —
London streets and young peo - ple   dy - ing. —

1. Mis - ter Death comes look-in'   for   a   home
2.   The down-ward roll-in'   die is   cast.   You bet - ter
3. No one seems to hear   them   call.

CHORUS

run   from the man   who wears the black cloak.

Got a big smile on his   face.   He'll

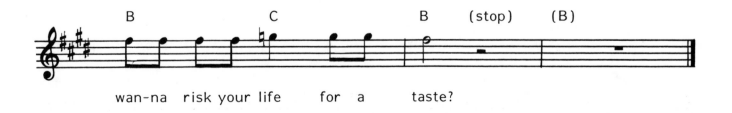

of - fer you for free,   the   ev - il in his hand. Do you

wan-na risk your life   for a   taste?

PLAIN JANE

Words and Music
by RUSS SHIPTON

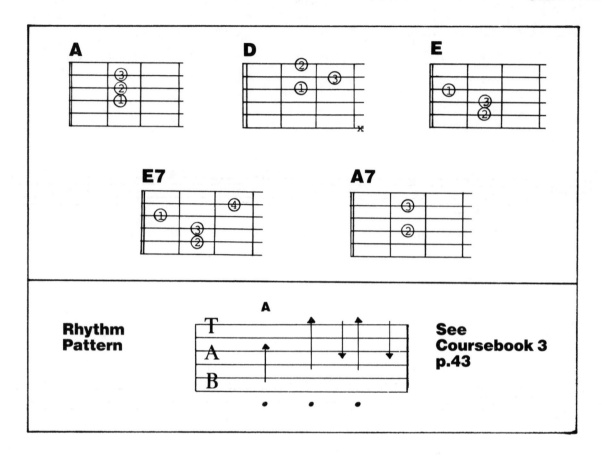

1. No one—— would call her beau-ti-ful,
2. school—— she would day - dream all day long,
3. When we—— got married, there was talk in the town,

but I nev-er—— liked the word "plain."
so she nev-er—— scored A's or B's,
how it was a shot-gun—— weddin' and I'd soon be playing

'Cause I can see that spar-kle—— in her eyes
but I know from the way—— she lives her
round. But she's my inspira - tion, —— my an-gel

VERSE 1 ONLY

When she smiles to hide all the pain.—— 2. And at

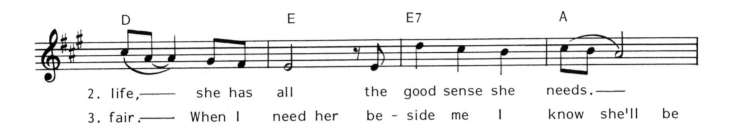

2. life,—— she has all the good sense she needs.——
3. fair.—— When I need her be - side me I know she'll be

CHORUS

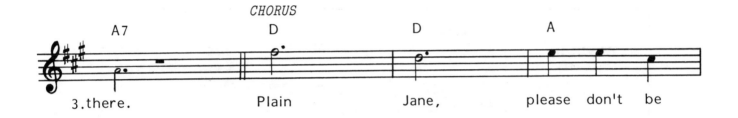

3.there. Plain Jane, please don't be

blue. Don't go listen-in'— to those lies — a -bout

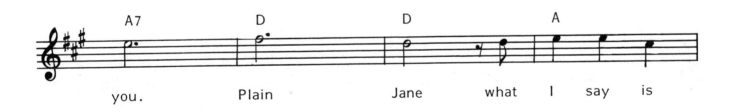

you. Plain Jane what I say is

true, Plain Jane, I love you.——

The Right Time

Words and Music
by RUSS SHIPTON

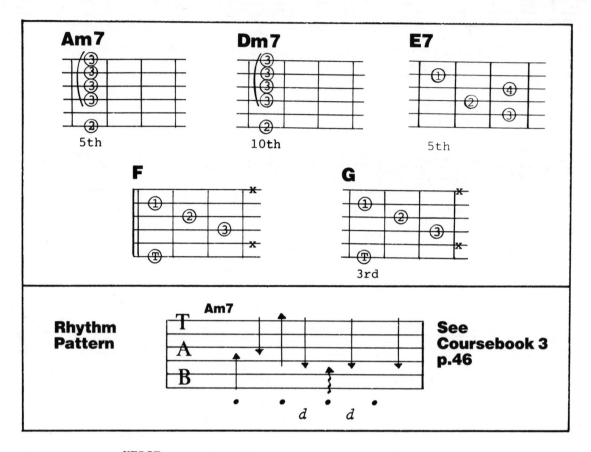

Am7   5th

Dm7   10th

E7   5th

F

G   3rd

Rhythm Pattern

Am7

See Coursebook 3 p.46

VERSE

Am7   Am7

1. I don't hear— what—— you're— say— in',—
2. When I was— just—— a — boy— I
3. There's three parts to eve —— ry— love— and—

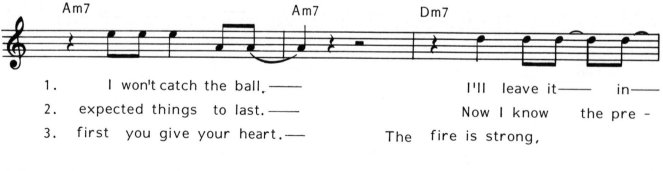

Am7   Am7   Dm7

1.   I won't catch the ball. ——   I'll leave it—— in——
2. expected things to last. ——   Now I know the pre -
3. first you give your heart. ——   The fire is strong,

Dm7   Am7   Am7

1. — your— court— and   let you win the call. ——
2. — ent— must— al - ways be-come the past. ——
3. no- thin's wrong—— 'cause Cu-pid's shot his dart. ——

1. You've turned me— in ——— side— out—and   now I guess we know,—
2. I've learnt to— acc———cept— the changes,   and here's a-noth— er one.—
3. As the road— twists—— and—turns— the   second phase will start.—

1. —   all   we can—— do is   shout,
2. —   It   was good—— while   it lasted, but
3. —   Then you'll be—— at   num-ber   three,when

CHORUS

1. so I—— bet-ter go.———————
2. now the — magic's gone.——————— Somethin'—tells ————— me—
3. it all— falls a-part.———————

it's— a-bout ———— time   I took my—bags—

—   and I   head-ed down the line.——   Some-thin'—tells—

—   me   it's— the right ——— time.————————

DON'T GIVE UP ON US

Words and Music
by TONY MACAULAY

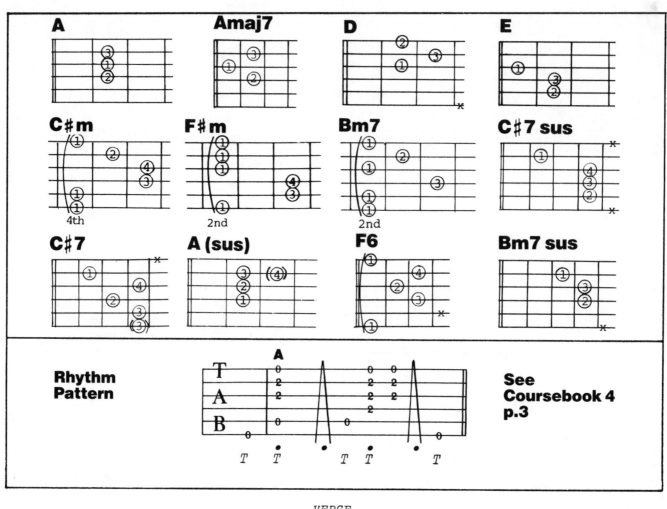

VERSE

1.Don't give up on us ba — by, don't make the wrong seem right, the fu-ture is-n't just one — night. It's writ-ten in the moon—light,—

2. up on us ba — by, we're still worth one more try, and though we put a last one—— by; just for a rain-y eve——ning,—

3. up on us ba — by, Lord knows we've come this far, why can't we stay the way we —— are? The an-gel and the dream—— er,—

1. *VERSE 1 ONLY*

D   A   Bm7   D   (stop)

and paint-ed in the stars,— we can't change ours.   2.Don't give

2.

D   C#7sus   C#7   D   A

2.when may - be stars are   few. }

3. who some-times plays the   fool. }   Don't give up on us, I—know

D   (stop)   A   Asus   A

we can still come through.   I

MIDDLE SECTION

F   F6   C

near - ly lost my head last — night,———   you've got a

Bm7sus   Bm7   A   C#7

right   to stop be- liev - ing.   There's still   a lit - tle—

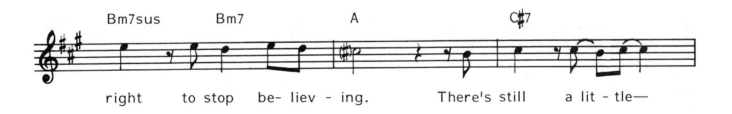

F#m   Bm7   D   (stop)

love left,   ev- en   so.   3.Don't give

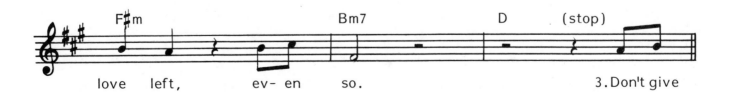

MOONDANCE

Words and Music
by VAN MORRISON

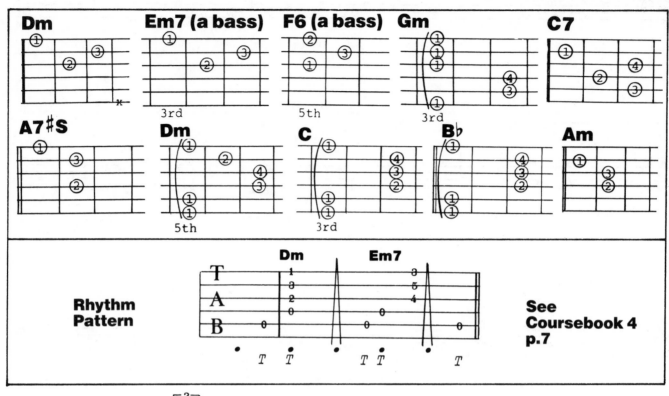

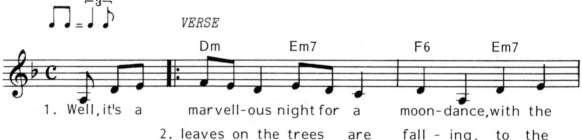

VERSE

Dm   Em7   F6   Em7

1. Well, it's a   marvell-ous night for a   moon-dance, with the
2. leaves on the trees   are   fall - ing, to the
3. wan-na make love to you   to-night.   I can't
4. come   my heart will be   wait - ing, to make

Dm   Em7   F6   Em7   Dm   Em7

1. stars   up a-bove in your   eyes.   A fan -   ta-bu-lous night to make
2. sound   of the breezes that   blow.   And I'm   try-ing to please to the
3. wait till the morning has   come.   And I know   now the time   is
4. sure that you're never a -   lone.   There and then   all my dreams will come

F6   Em7   Dm   Em7   F6   Em7

1. ro-mance, 'neath the   cov-er of   Oc-to-ber   skies. 2. And all the
2. call - ing   of   your heartstrings that play soft and   low.   And all the
3. just right, and straight in-to my   arms you will   run. 4. And when you
4. true, girl. There   and   then I will make you my   own.   And eve-ry

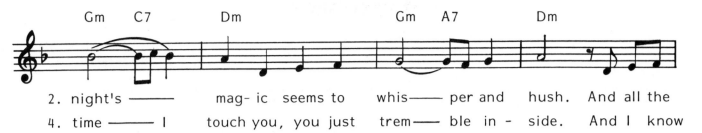

Gm   C7   Dm   Gm   A7   Dm

2. night's ——— mag-ic seems to whis——per and hush. And all the
4. time ——— I touch you, you just trem——ble in - side. And I know

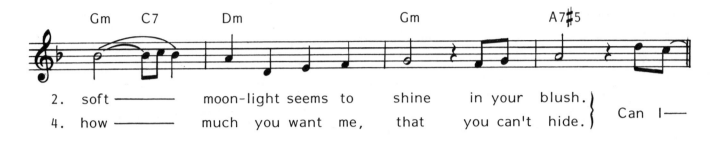

Gm   C7   Dm   Gm   A7♯5

2. soft ——————— moon-light seems to shine in your blush.)
4. how ——————— much you want me, that you can't hide.) Can I——

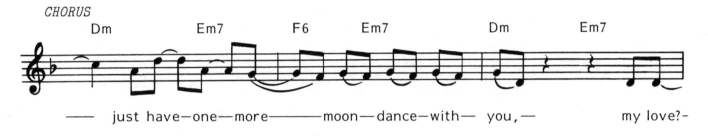

CHORUS
Dm   Em7   F6   Em7   Dm   Em7

—— just have—one—more———moon—dance—with— you, ——   my love?-

F6   Em7   Dm   Em7   F6   Em7

—   Can I —— just make—some— more —— ro—mance—with you—

Dm   Em7   F6 A7 (stop)   ENDING   Dm (5th pos)   C (3rd pos)

—   my love?—   3. Well I Can't I —— just have— one

B♭   Am   Gm (3rd pos)   Dm

more — moon-dance— with you, my— love?———

BO DIDDLEY

Words and Music
by ELLAS McDANIEL

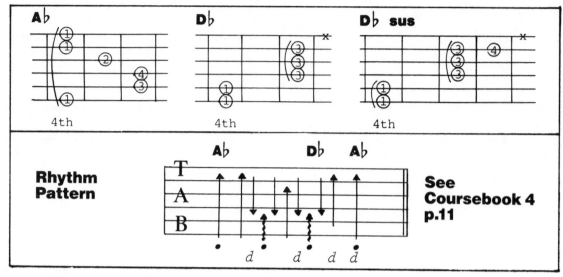

Rhythm Pattern

See Coursebook 4 p.11

1. Bo Diddley buy you a dia - mond ring.
2. Bo Diddley caught a nan - ny goat,   to
3. Won't you come to my house and rock that bone?
4. Bo Diddley, Bo Diddley, have you heard?

1. If that dia - mond ring don't shine,——
2. make his baby a Sun - day coat.——
3. Take my ba - by all the way home.——
4. My pretty ba - by said she was a bird.——

VERSE 1 ONLY   *VERSES 1, 2, 3, 4.*

1. He's gonna take it to a private eye.

1. If that pri-vate eye can't see,
2. Bo Diddley caught a bear cat,
3. Look at that bodo, oh where's he been?
4. Bo Diddley play on your gui-tar,

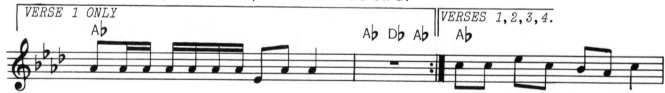

1. he bet-ter not take that ring from me.
2. to make his baby a Sun - day hat.
3. Up to your house and gone a- gain.
4. rhythm so sweet from Af - ri - ca.

NEVER GOIN' BACK AGAIN

Words and Music
by LINDSAY BUCKINGHAM

See Coursebook 4 p.11

VERSE

1. She broke down and let me in.
2. You don't know what it means to win.

Made me see where I'd
Come on down and see me a-

been.
gain.

CHORUS

Been down one time, been down two times,

Mm, nev-er go-in' back a- gain.

YOU NEEDED ME

Words and Music
by RANDY GOODRUM

Rhythm Pattern

See Coursebook 4 p.15

1. I cried a tear, you wiped it dry. I was con-
2. hand, when it was cold. When I was

fused, you cleared my mind. I sold my soul, you bought it
lost, you took me home. You gave me hope, when I was

back for me,— and held me up, and gave me dig-ni-ty.— Some-how you
at the end,— you turned my lies back in-to truth a-gain.— You ev-en

need-ed me. } You gave me strength, to stand a-lone a-gain,— to face the
called me friend. }

world out on my own a-gain.— You put me high up-on a

ped-es-tal,— so high that I can al-most see e-ter-ni-ty,— you

need-ed me,— you need-ed me,— And I can't be-lieve it's you, I can't be-

lieve it's true, I need-ed you— and you were there.— And I'll

never leave, why should I leave, I'd be a fool, 'cause I've finally found someone who really

ENDING

cares. 2. You held my need-ed me,— you

need-ed me,— you need-ed me.—

STAIRWAY TO HEAVEN

Words and Music by
JIMMY PAGE and ROBERT PLANT

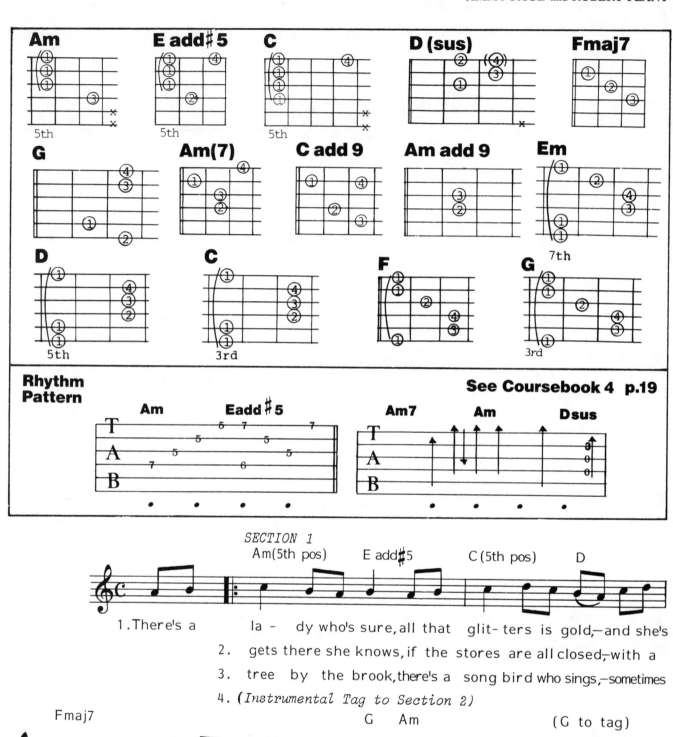

Am   E add♯5   C   D (sus)   Fmaj7

G   Am(7)   C add 9   Am add 9   Em

D   C   F   G

Rhythm Pattern

See Coursebook 4 p.19

Am   Eadd♯5   Am7   Am   Dsus

SECTION 1

Am(5th pos)   E add♯5   C (5th pos)   D

1. There's a la - dy who's sure, all that glit- ters is gold,— and she's

2. gets there she knows, if the stores are all closed,— with a

3. tree by the brook, there's a song bird who sings,— sometimes

4. (Instrumental Tag to Section 2)

Fmaj7   G Am   (G to tag)

1. buy - ing a stair - way— to hea - ven.—   When she

2. word she can get what— she came for.—

3. all of our thoughts are— mis - giv - en.—

C   D   Fmaj7   Am add 9   C   G

Ooh,—— ooh, ——— and she's buy— ing a stair— way to

© 1972 Superhype Publishing
Warner Bros Music Ltd, 17 Berners Street, London W1P 3DD

hea-ven.— There's a sign on the wall,—but she wants to be sure—'cause you

SECTION 2

know sometimes words have two mean—ings. 3.In a

Ooh,— it makes me won-der.—

1. There's a feel - ing I get when I look to the west, and my
2. And it's whis- pered that soon if we all call the tune, then the

1. spi - rit is cry-ing for leav——ing.— In my thoughts I have seen rings of
2. pi - per will lead us to reas—— on.— And a new day will dawn for

1. smoke through the trees,and the voic- es of those who stand look——ing.—
2. those who stand long,and the for-ests will ech-o with laugh—ter.—

34

1. If there's a bris-tle in your hedge-row,—don't be al-armed now. —
2. Your head is hum-ming and it won't go,— in case you don't know,—

1. It's just a spring clean for the May queen,—
2. the pi—per's call - ing you to join him.——

1. Yes, there are two paths you can go by,—but in the long run,—
2. Dear la - dy can you hear the wind blow,—and did you know,—

1. there's still time to change— the road —you're on.
2. your stairway lies on the——whis-per——ing wind?

TAG TO LEAD BREAK

LEAD BREAK

SECTION 3

35

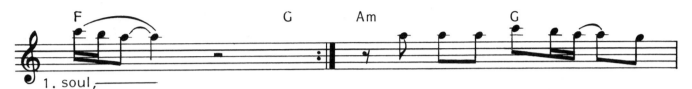

1. And as we wind on down the road,   our shadows taller than our
2. there walks a la - dy we all   know,   who shines white light and wants to
3. how ev-erything still turns to   gold.   And if you lis - ten ve-ry

1. soul,————
2. show,————   the tune will come to you—   at
3. hard,————

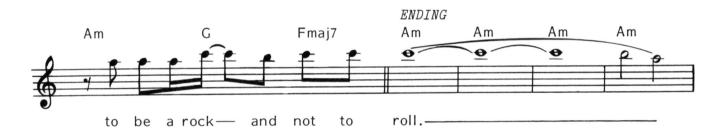

last,   when all are one and one is   all,————

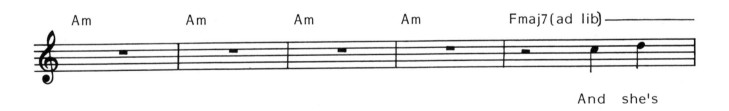

ENDING

to be a rock— and not to   roll.————

And she's

hold chord

buy —— ing a stair— way—   to hea-ven.————

WALKING ON THE MOON

Words and Music
by STING

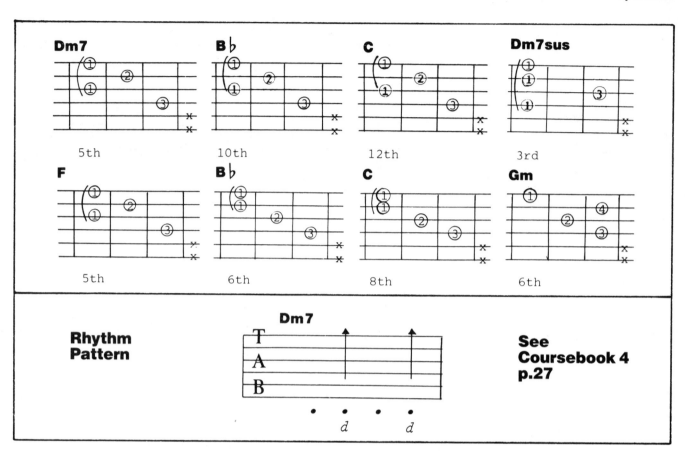

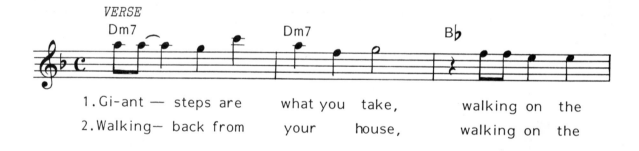

VERSE

1. Gi-ant — steps are what you take, walking on the
2. Walking— back from your house, walking on the

moon. I hope my legs don't break,
moon. Walking back from your house,

walking on the moon. We could —walk for - ev - er,
walking on the moon. Feet they —hard-ly touch the ground,

walk-ing on the moon. — We could— be to - geth - er,
walk-ing on the moon.— My feet don't—hard-ly make no sound,

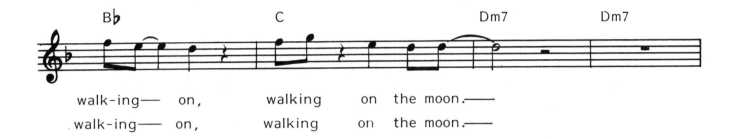

walk-ing— on, walking on the moon.——
walk-ing— on, walking on the moon.——

MIDDLE SECTION

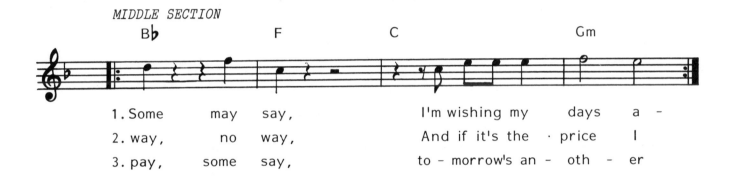

1. Some may say, I'm wishing my days a -
2. way, no way, And if it's the price I
3. pay, some say, to - morrow's an - oth - er

day, you'll stay I may as well play.

ENDING

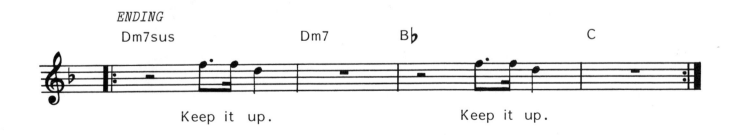

Keep it up. Keep it up.

WHAT'S LOVE GOT TO DO WITH IT?

Words and Music by
GRAHAM LYLE and TERRY BRITTEN

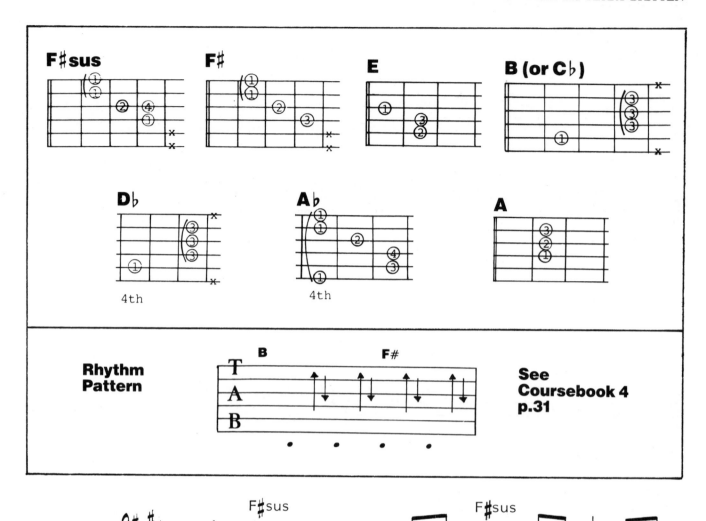

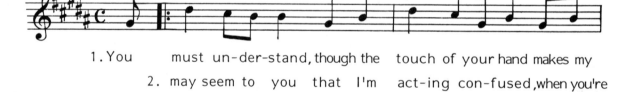

1. You   must un-der-stand, though the   touch of your hand makes my

2. may seem to   you   that I'm   act-ing con-fused, when you're

pulse re-act; —   that it's on - ly the thrill   of

close   to me. —   If I   tend   to look dazed,   I

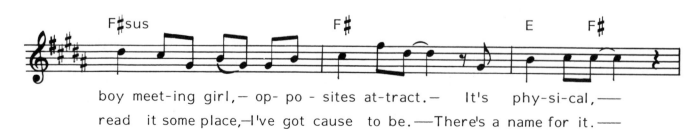

boy meet-ing girl, — op-po - sites at-tract. —   It's phy-si-cal, ——

read it some place, —I've got cause to be. —There's a name for it. ——

Note: Last Chorus is one tone (2 frets) higher than before. Move guitar shapes up 2 frets.

GHOSTS IN MY MUSIC

Words and Music
by RUSS SHIPTON

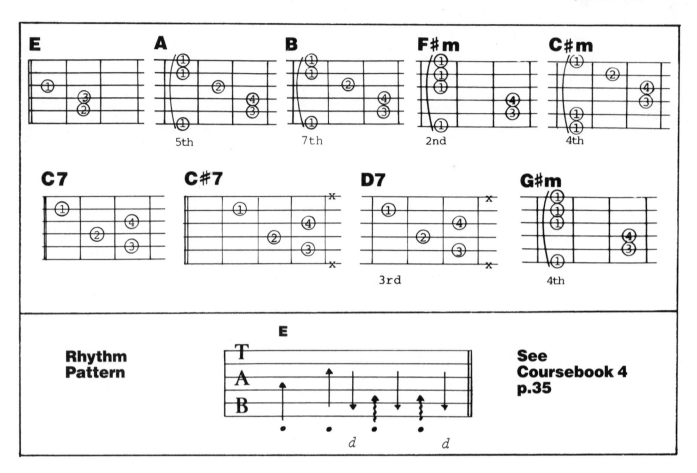

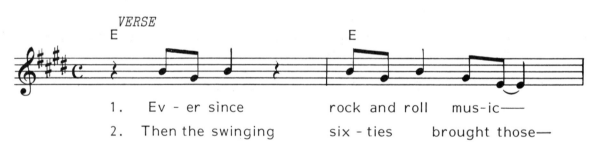

Rhythm Pattern

See Coursebook 4 p.35

VERSE

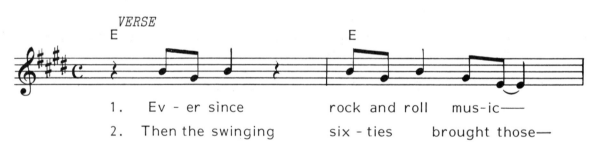

1. Ev - er since   rock and roll   mus-ic——
2. Then the swinging   six - ties   brought those——

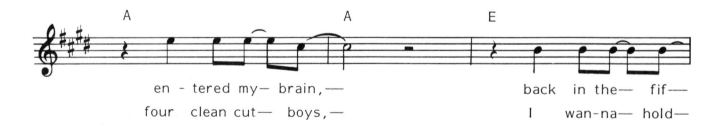

en - tered my— brain,——   back in the— fif—
four clean cut— boys,—   I wan-na— hold—

—— ties,— Lord— I've—   nev - er been the same.——
—— your— hand,— and   then all the glitter and noise.——

© 1985 Russ Shipton

42

MIDDLE SECTION

Now the   ci-gar— smo— kin'—   mo-gul star -mak-er

wants some more songs from   me.——   He says the   word, but he doesn't know the

mean-ing—   of or - ig -in - al - i - ty.———

As long as he gets— a   high-er stake   he'll

feel like giv-in' me   mine,—   but those   ghosts— in— my— mu—

— sic and me,—   we know that it's a crime.————   Yes, there's

BROKEN MAN

Words and Music
by RUSS SHIPTON

JOHNNY B. GOODE

Words and Music
by CHUCK BERRY

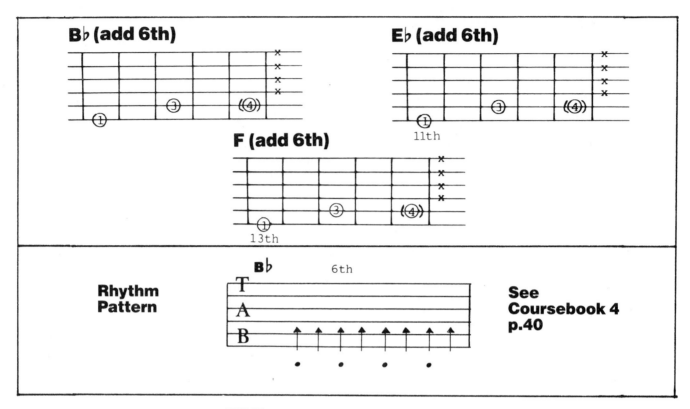

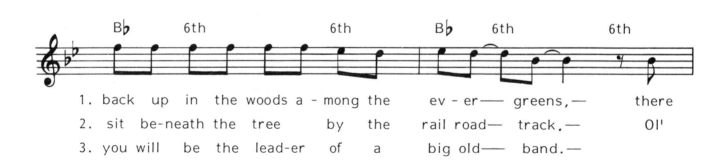

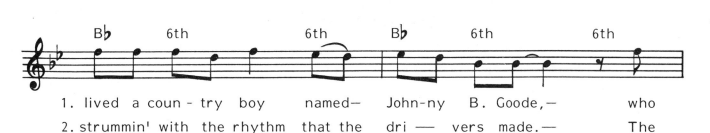

1. lived a coun - try boy named— John-ny B. Goode,— who
2. strummin' with the rhythm that the dri — vers made.— The
3. hear you play your music till the sun— goes down.— May -

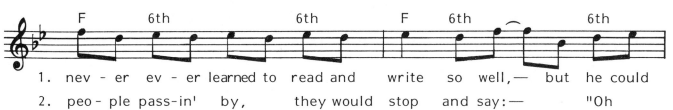

1. nev - er ev - er learned to read and write so well,— but he could
2. peo - ple pass-in' by, they would stop and say:— "Oh
3. be some day your name will be in lights, a - say-in'

1. play a gui - tar — just like a ring- in' a bell.—
2. my but that lit — tle coun- try boy can play!" ⎫
3. "John-ny B. Goode — to — night." ⎭ Go

CHORUS

go!   Go,Johnny go!   Go!   Go, Johnny go!

Go!   Go Johnny go!   Go!   Go Johnny go!

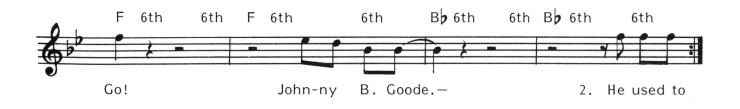

Go!   John-ny B. Goode.—   2. He used to

LAYLA

Words and Music by
ERIC CLAPTON and JIM GORDON

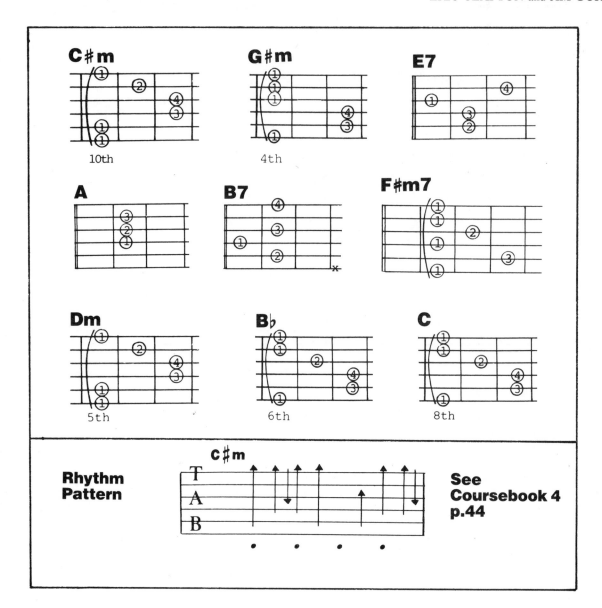

Rhythm Pattern

See Coursebook 4 p.44

VERSE

1. What will you do when you get lone-ly,—
2. Tried to give you con-so-la-tion,—
3. Let's make the best of the sit-u-a-tion,—

1. with no-bo-dy wait-ing by your side?
2. when your old man had let you down.
3. be-fore I fina-lly go in-sane.

A　　　　　　B7　　　　　　E　　　　　A

1. You've been run-ning, 　and　　hid - ing much too　long, —
2. Like　a　fool, 　　I　　　fell　in　love with you, —
3. Please don't say, 　we'll　nev - er find　a　way, —

F#m7　　　　　　B7　　　　　　E(stop)　　(A)

1. you know it's　just your fool— ish　　pride.
2. turned the whole world　up —side　　down.　}　Lay —
3. and tell　me　all　my love's— in　　vain.

CHORUS
Dm　　　Bb　　　　　　　C　　　　Dm

la, ——　　　　　　you　got me on—— my knees. Lay -

Dm　Bb　　　　　C　　　Dm　　　　Dm　　Bb

la, ——　　I'm beg-ging, dar-ling, please. Lay - la, ——

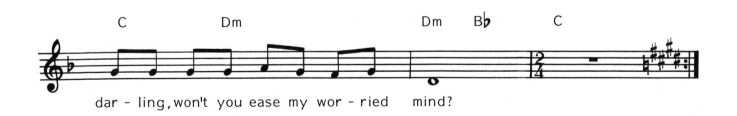

C　　　　Dm　　　　　　　Dm　Bb　C

dar - ling, won't you ease my wor - ried　mind?

CATCH IT

Words and Music
by RUSS SHIPTON

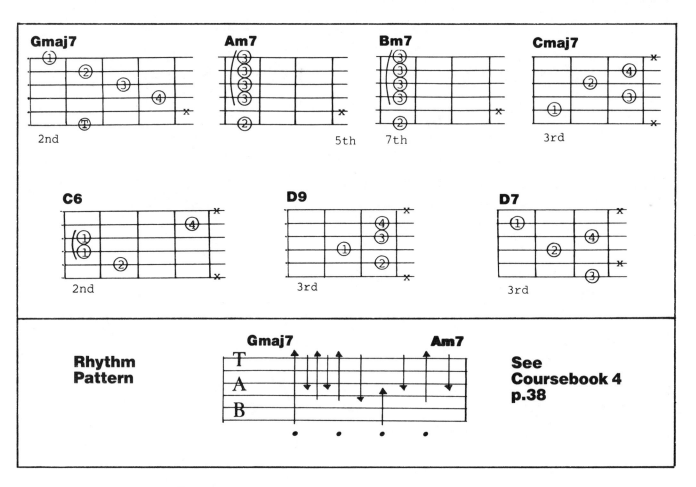

See Coursebook 4 p.38

Note: The first note of this instrumental piece (F♯) is played at the 7th fret, 2nd string

RUSS SHIPTON'S Rock & Pop Guitar Songbook 3

Contents

Note: The songs in this book provide more practice material for "Russ Shiptons Rock & Pop Guitar" course. References are given to guitar styles and techniques covered in coursebooks 1 & 2 which can be used to play these additional songs.

First Published 1986
© International Music Publications

Exclusive Distributors
International Music Publications
Southend Road, Woodford Green,
Essex IG8 8HN, England.

Printed in England by JB Offset (Marks Tey) Limited
Marks Tey, Essex.

215-2-342

WORDS

Words and Music by
BARRY, ROBIN and MAURICE GIBB

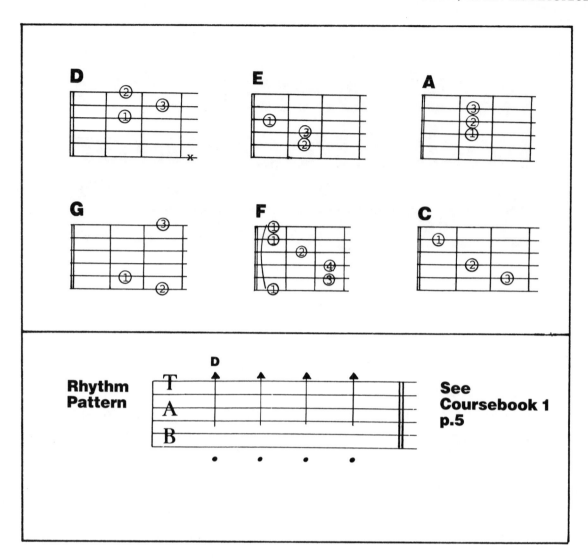

gone, 'cause that would bring a tear to me. This
life, I'm here if you should call to me. You

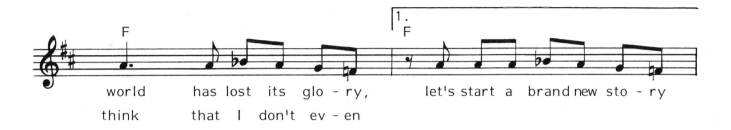

world has lost its glo - ry, let's start a brand new sto - ry
think that I don't ev - en

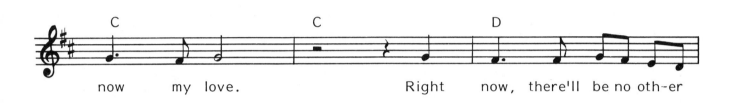

now my love. Right now, there'll be no oth-er

time, and I can show you how, my love

mean a sin-gle word I say. It's on - ly

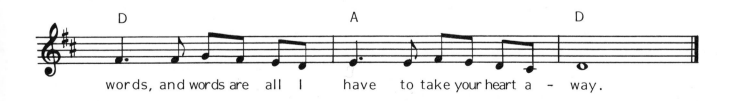

words, and words are all I have to take your heart a - way.

I FEEL LIKE BUDDY HOLLY

Words and Music
by MIKE BATT

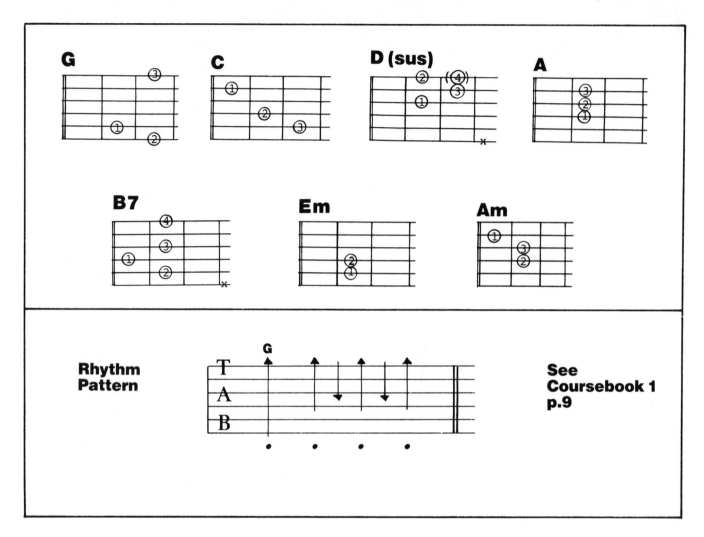

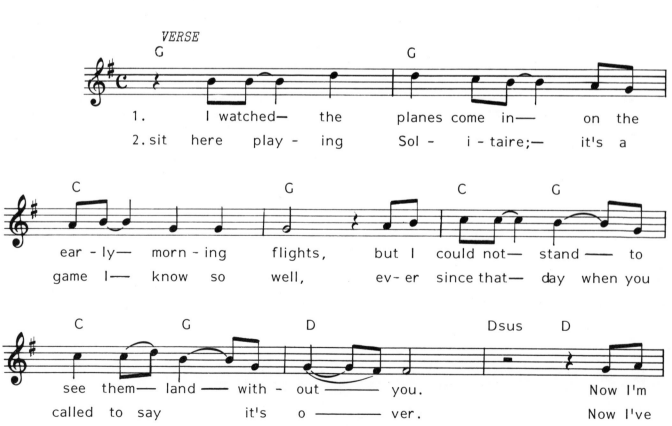

VERSE

G   G

1. I watched— the planes come in— on the
2. sit here play-ing Sol-i-taire;— it's a

C   G   C   G

ear-ly— morn-ing flights, but I could not— stand — to
game I know so well, ev-er since that— day when you

C   G   D   Dsus   D

see them— land — with-out —— you. Now I'm
called to say it's o —— ver. Now I've

IT DOESN'T MATTER ANY MORE

Words and Music
by PAUL ANKA

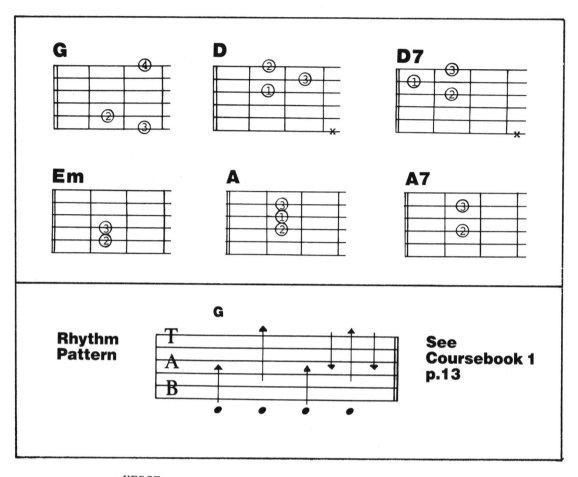

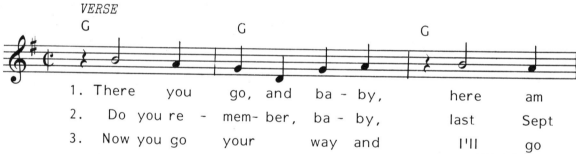

VERSE

1. There you go, and ba - by, here am
2. Do you re - mem- ber, ba - by, last Sept
3. Now you go your way and I'll go

1. I. Well, you left me here so I would
2.- em - ber, how you held me tight each and
3. mine, now and for - ev - er, till the

1. sit and cry. Well,— goll - y
2. ev - 'ry night? Well,— whoops - a
3. end of time. I'll find some - bo - dy

1. gee, what have you done to me? I
2. dais - y, how you drove me cra - zy. I
3. new, and ba - by, you say we're through, and

1. guess it does - n't mat - ter an - y - more.
2. guess it does - n't mat - ter an - y - more.
3. you won't mat - ter an - y - more.

MIDDLE SECTION

There's no use in me a - cry ——————

———— in', I've done ev - 'ry - thing, and now I'm sick of

try—— in', I've thrown a - way my days, was - ted all my

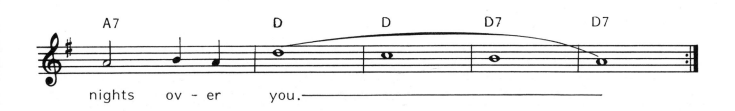

nights ov - er you.————————

KING OF THE ROAD

Words and Music
by ROGER MILLER

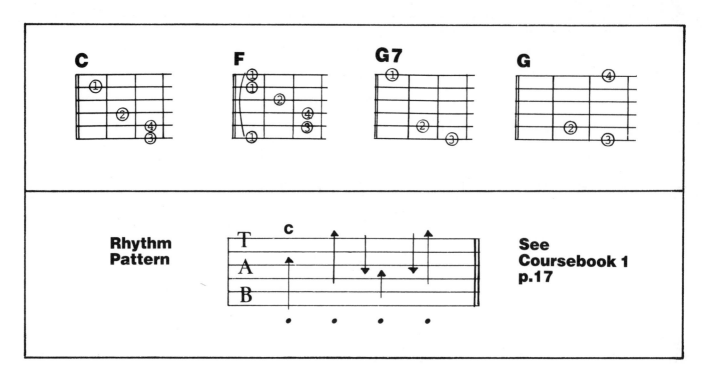

Rhythm Pattern

See Coursebook 1 p.17

1. & 3. Trail-er —— for sale or rent.——
2. Third box—— car, mid - night train;——

Rooms —— to let fif - ty cents.—— No phone,—— no
des —— ti-nation Ban - gor, Maine.—— Old worn—— out

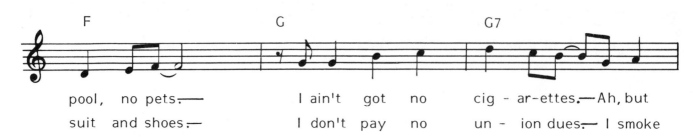

pool, no pets.—— I ain't got no cig - ar-ettes.——Ah, but
suit and shoes.—— I don't pay no un - ion dues.—— I smoke

two hours— of push-ing broom-buys a eight — by twelve,
old sto——gies I have found, short,— but not too

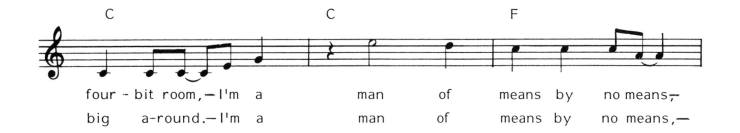

four - bit room,—I'm a man of means by no means,—
big a-round.—I'm a man of means by no means,—

king of the road! road! I know
king of the

MIDDLE SECTION

ev-e-ry en-gin-eer on ev-e-ry train,— all of the child-ren,—and

all of their names,— and ev-e-ry hand-out— in ev-e-ry town,— and

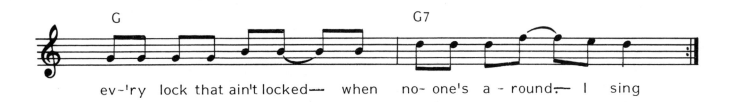

ev-'ry lock that ain't locked— when no-one's a-round.— I sing

WILD COUNTRY DREAM

Words and Music
by RUSS SHIPTON ·

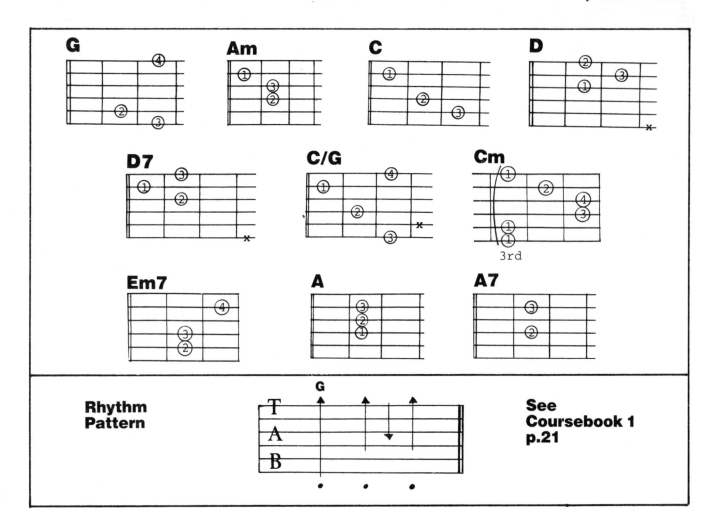

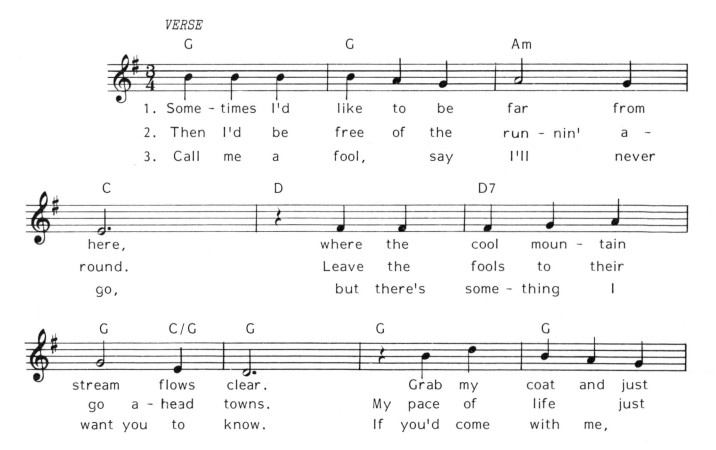

ARE YOU LONESOME TONIGHT

Words and Music by
ROY TURK and LOU HANDMAN

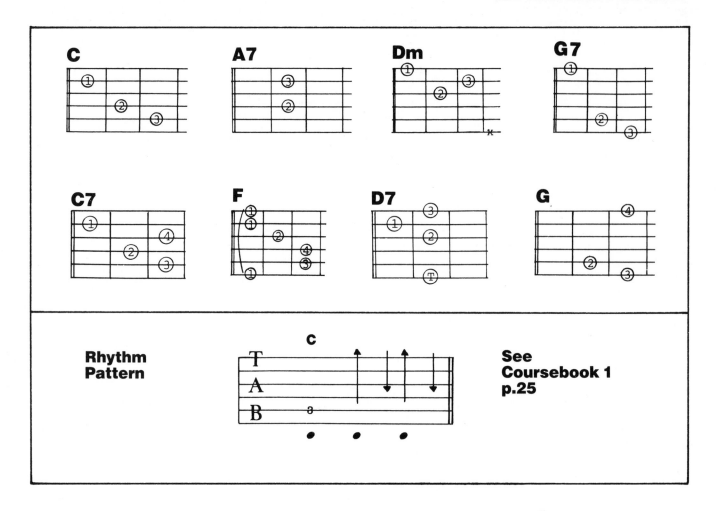

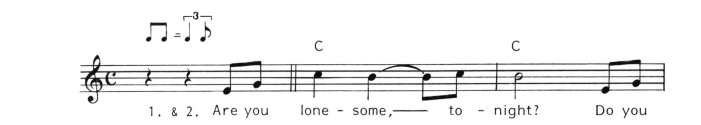

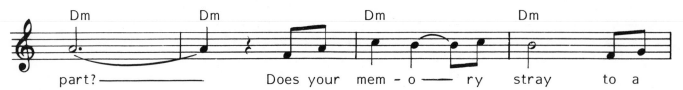

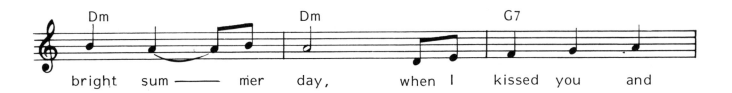

bright sum —— mer day, when I kissed you and

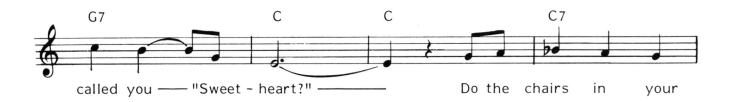

called you —— "Sweet - heart?" —————— Do the chairs in your

par - lour —— seem emp - ty and bare? Do you gaze at your

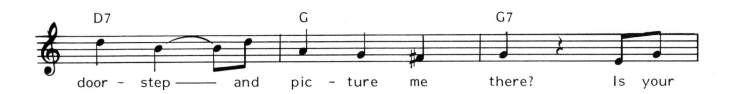

door - step —— and pic - ture me there? Is your

heart filled —— with pain? Shall I come back —— a - gain? Tell me

dear, are you lone - some to - night? 2. Are you

RECITATION

I wonder if you're lonely tonight?
You know, someone said the world's a stage and each must play a part.
Fate had me playing 'in love', with you as my sweetheart.
Act one was where we met. I loved you at first glance.
You read your lines so cleverly and never missed a cue.
Then came Act Two. You seemed to change, you acted strange.
And why, I'll never know.
Honey you lied when you said you loved me, and I had no cause to doubt you.
But I'd rather go on hearing your lies than to go on living without you.
Now the stage is bare, and I'm standing there with emptiness all around.
And if you won't come back to me, then they can ring the curtain down.

(After recitation, sing "Is your heart" etc.)

WHEN WILL I BE LOVED

Words and Music
by PHIL EVERLY

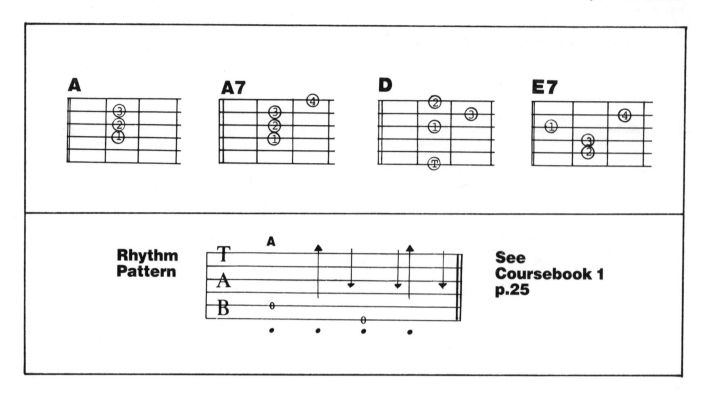

Rhythm Pattern

See Coursebook 1 p.25

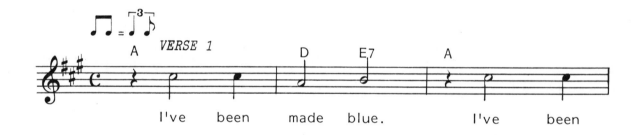

VERSE 1

| A | D | E7 | A |

I've been made blue. I've been

| D | E7 | A | D | E7 | A |

lied to. When will I be loved?

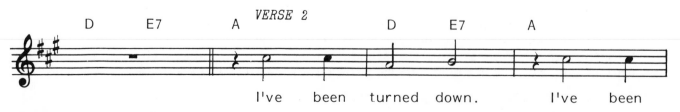

VERSE 2

| D | E7 | A | D | E7 | A |

I've been turned down. I've been

pushed round. When will I be loved?

MIDDLE SECTION

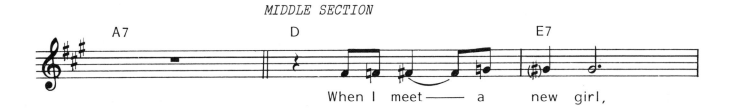

When I meet —— a new girl,

that I want —— for mine, she al - ways breaks my

heart in two.— It hap - pens ev - 'ry time.

VERSE 3

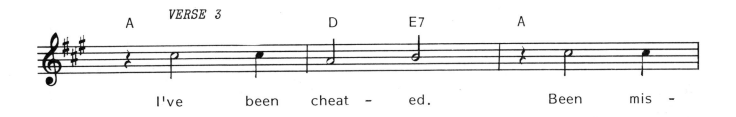

I've been cheat - ed. Been mis -

treat - ed. When will I be loved?

CATHY'S CLOWN

Words and Music by
DON EVERLY and PHIL EVERLY

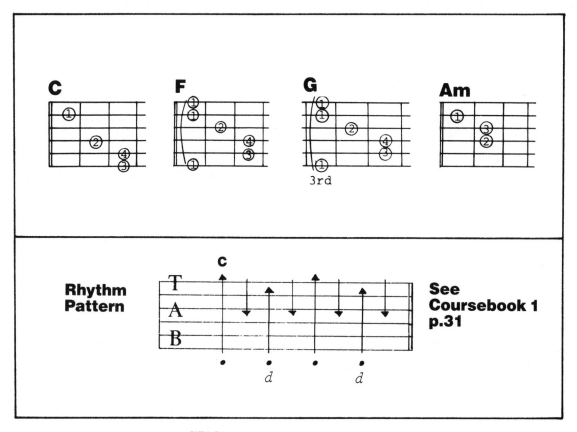

VERSE

1. I've got to stand tall.
2. When you see me shed a tear,

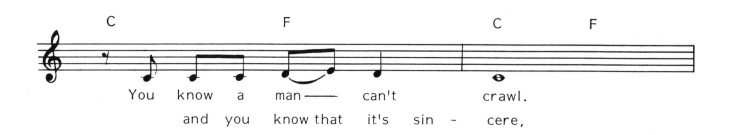

You know a man — can't crawl.
and you know that it's sin - cere,

For when he knows you tell lies, and he lets them pass
don't you think it's kind - a sad that you're treat-ing me so

by,   then   he's   not   a   man   at   all.
bad,   or   don't   you   ev –   en   care?

CHORUS

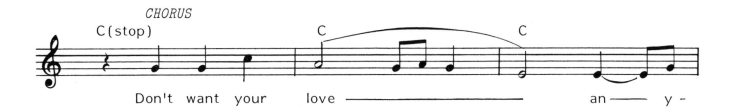

Don't   want   your   love ——————————————————— an ——— y –

more.   Don't   want   your   kiss ————————————————

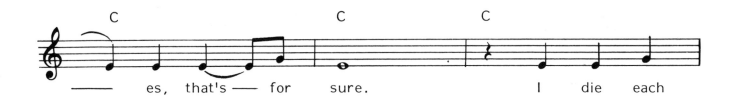

—— es, that's —— for   sure.   I   die   each

time   I   hear —— this   sound.   Here   he

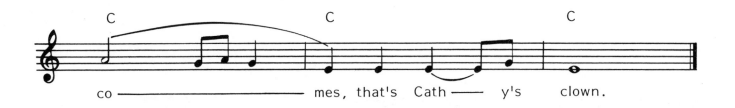

co —————————————— mes, that's Cath ——— y's   clown.

(IN THE) MIDNIGHT HOUR

Words and Music by
WILSON PICKETT and STEVE CROPPER

1. I'm gon-na   wait   till the mid-night—
2. wait   till the stars come—

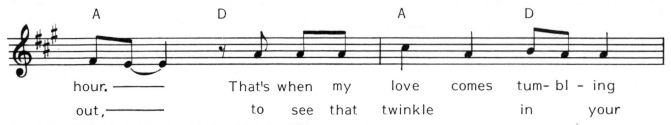

hour. ——   That's when   my   love   comes   tum-bl-ing
out, ——   to   see   that   twinkle   in   your

down. ———— I'm gon - na wait till the mid- night—
eye. ———— I'm gon - na wait till the mid- night—

hour, ———— when there's no one else a —
hour, ———— when my love be - gins to

round. I'm gon - na take you— girl,— and
shine. You're the on - ly — girl — I

hold you, and do all—— the things I
know, that real - ly—— loves me

told you, in the mid-night — hour. ————
so, in the mid-night — hour. ————

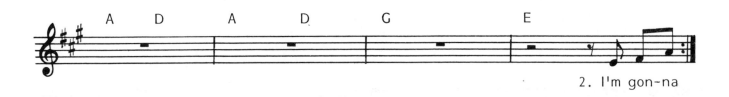

2. I'm gon-na

NOBODY TOLD ME

Words and Music
by JOHN LENNON

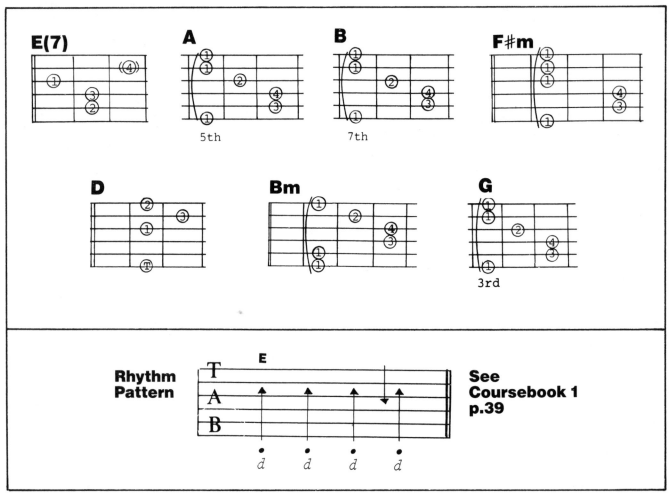

1. Ev'ry bo-dy's talk—in' and no-one says— a word.—
2. Ev'ry bo-dy's run—nin' and no-one makes—a move.—
3. Ev'ry bo-dy's smo-kin' and no-one's get—tin' high.—

Ev-'ry bo——dy's mak-in' love,and no-one real— ly cares.— There's
Ev-'ry bo—dy's a win-ner I've got nothin' left— to lose.— There's a
Ev-'ry bo——dy's fly - in', and nev-er touch-the sky.— There's

Na-zis in— the bath— room just be - low the stairs.—
lit - tle yell— ow id—— ol to the north of Kat-man - du. ——
U. F. O's— ov-er New York, and I ain't too sur - prised.*(To Tag and Chorus)*

Al-ways some—thin' happ—'nin' and nothin's go— in' on.— There's
Ev-'ry- bo— dy's fly——in' and no one leaves—the ground.— For

al-ways some—thin' cook— in', and nothin' in— the pot.— They're
ev-'ry- bo— dy's cry——in', and no one makes— a sound. There's a

star-vin' back—in Chi— na, so fin – ish what you've got.
place for us——in mov— ies, you just got - ta lay a - round.

TAG TO CHORUS

CHORUS

Nobody told me there'd—be days—like these.— Nobody told me there'd—be days—

—— like these.— Nobody told me there'd-be days—like these.—

Strange days in-deed!—— *(Spoken)*1. Strange days indeed!
2. Most peculiar momma!

BEST OF ALL

Words and Music
by RUSS SHIPTON

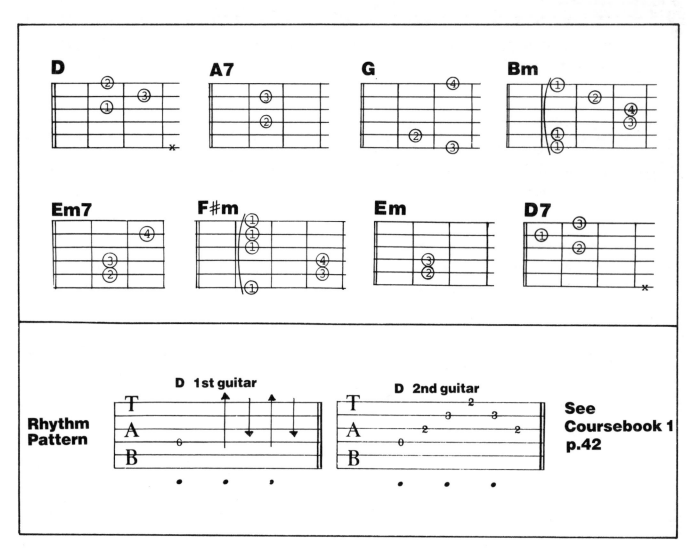

See Coursebook 1 p.42

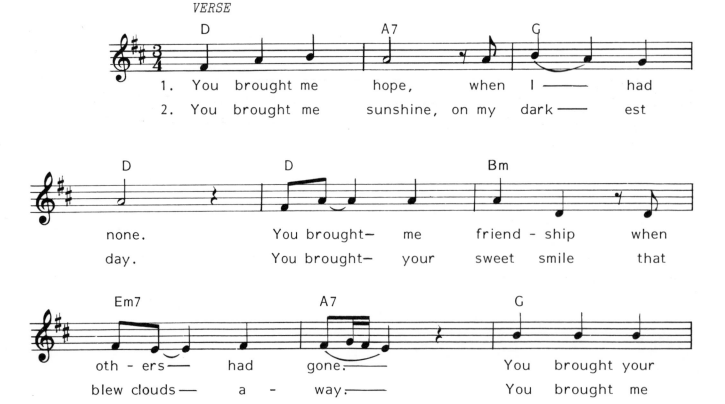

VERSE

D   A7   G

1. You brought me hope, when I —— had
2. You brought me sunshine, on my dark —— est

D   D   Bm

none.   You brought— me friend - ship when
day.   You brought— your sweet smile that

Em7   A7   G

oth - ers—— had gone.—— You brought your
blew clouds—— a - way.— You brought me

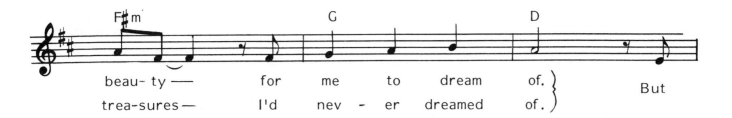

beau-ty —— for me to dream of.
trea-sures — I'd nev - er dreamed of.

But

best —— of all dar— ling,— you brought me

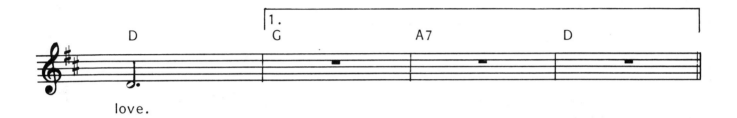

1.

love.

2.

MIDDLE SECTION

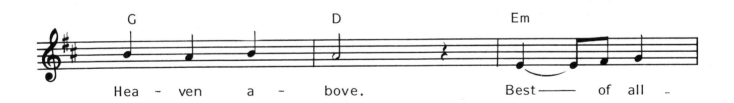

Love, love, from

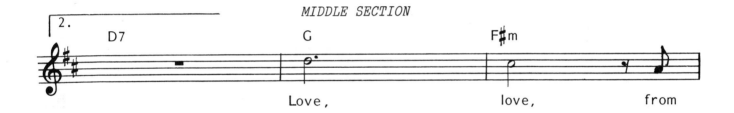

Hea - ven a - bove. Best —— of all

dar— ling,— you brought me love.

VISIT TO NEW ENGLAND

Words and Music
by RUSS SHIPTON

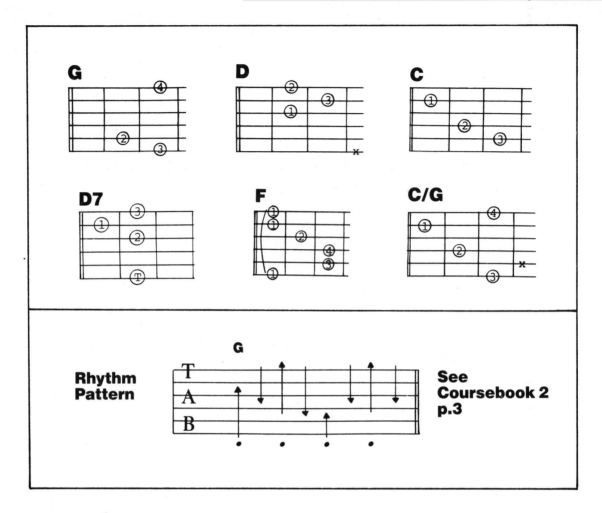

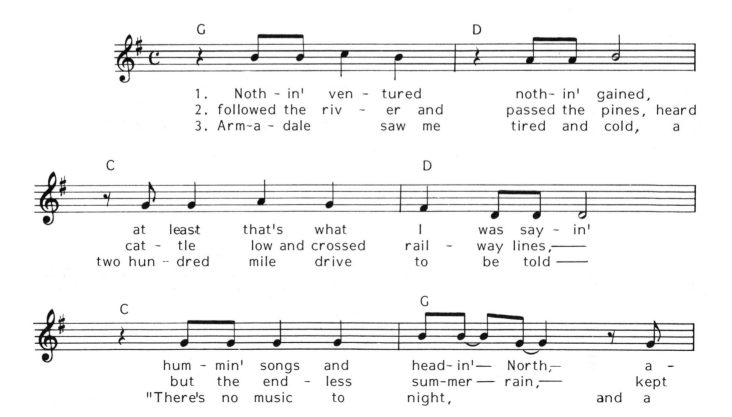

1. Noth - in' ven - tured   noth- in' gained,
2. followed the riv - er and   passed the pines, heard
3. Arm-a-dale saw me   tired and cold, a

at least   that's   what   I   was say - in'
cat - tle   low and crossed   rail - way lines,——
two hun - dred   mile   drive   to   be told ——

hum - min' songs and   head- in'— North,—   a -
but the end - less   sum-mer — rain,—   kept
"There's no music to   night,   and a

SWEET CAROLINE

Words and Music
by NEIL DIAMOND

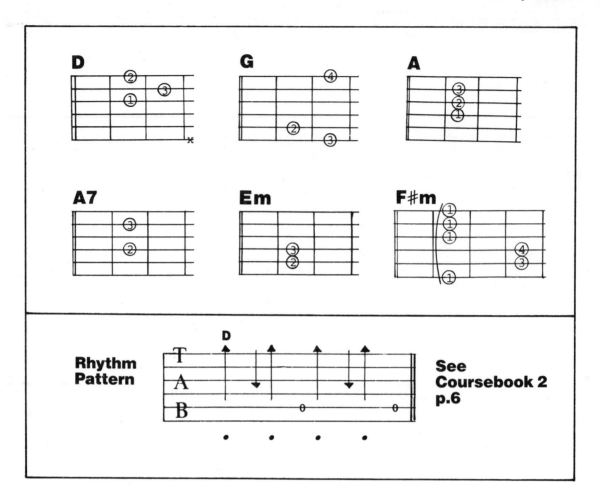

© 1969 & 1986 Stonebridge Music, USA
Warner Bros Music Ltd, 17 Berners Street, London W1P 3DD

ROCK & ROLL MUSIC

Words and Music
by CHUCK BERRY

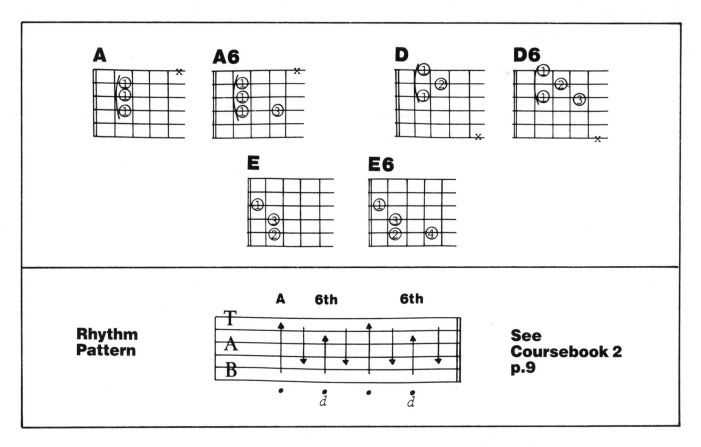

Rhythm Pattern

See Coursebook 2 p.9

Just let me hear some of that rock and roll——

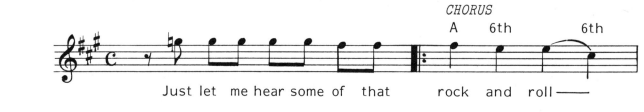

mu - sic, an-y old way you choose it. It's got a

back beat, you can't— lose it, an-y old time you use——

— it. It's got-ta be rock 'n' roll mu - sic,

if you wan-na dance with me,——   if you wan-na dance with me.—

VERSE

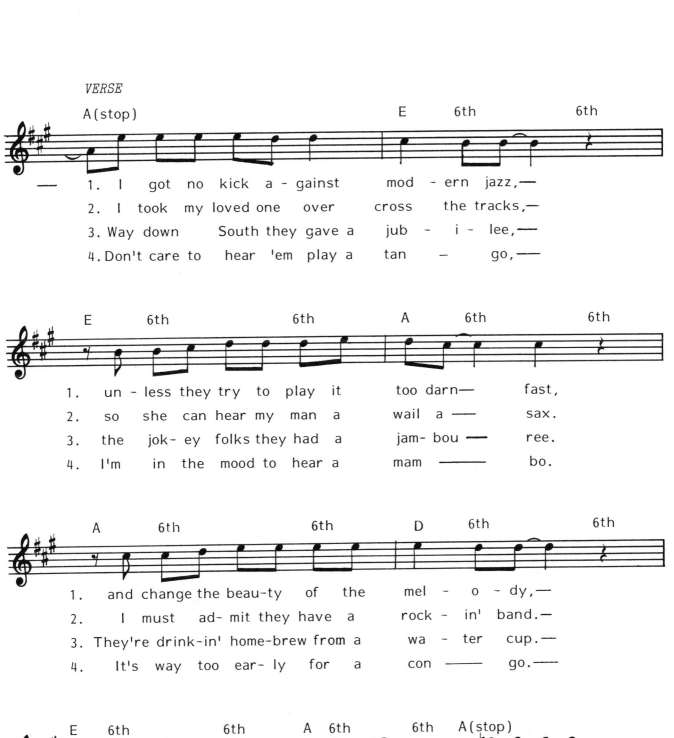

1. I got no kick a - gainst   mod - ern jazz,—
2. I took my loved one over   cross   the tracks,—
3. Way down   South they gave a   jub - i - lee,—
4. Don't care to   hear 'em play a   tan —   go,—

1. un - less they try to play it   too darn—   fast,
2. so she can hear my man a   wail a ——   sax.
3. the jok- ey folks they had a   jam- bou ——   ree.
4. I'm in the mood to hear a   mam ———   bo.

1. and change the beau-ty of the   mel - o - dy,—
2. I must ad- mit they have a   rock - in' band.—
3. They're drink-in' home-brew from a   wa - ter cup.—
4. It's way too ear- ly for a   con —— go.——

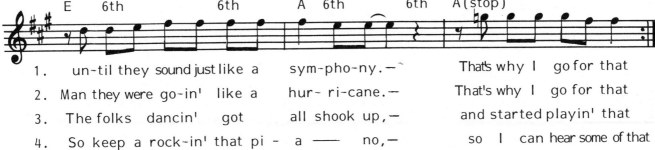

1. un-til they sound just like a   sym-pho-ny.—   That's why I   go for that
2. Man they were go-in' like a   hur- ri-cane.—   That's why I   go for that
3. The folks dancin' got   all shook up,—   and started playin' that
4. So keep a rock-in' that pi - a —— no,—   so I can hear some of that

GREAT BALLS OF FIRE

Words and Music by
JACK HAMMER and OTIS BLACKWELL

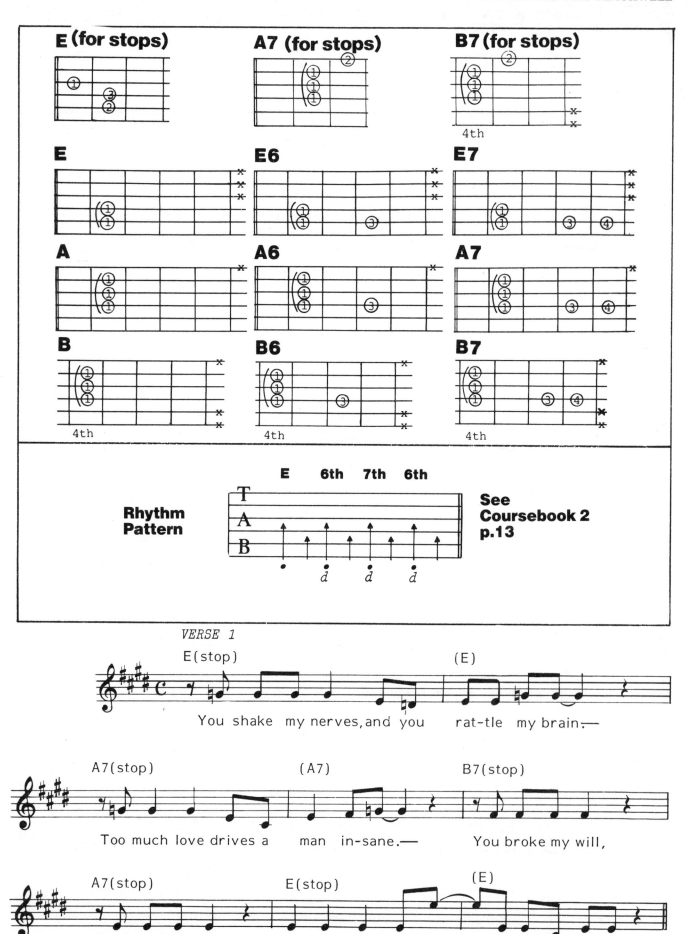

© 1957 & 1986 BRS Music Corp
All Rights Assigned Chappell & Co Inc, USA
Carlin Music Corporation, 14 New Burlington Street, London W1X 2LR
International Copyright Secured   All Rights Reserved

SWEET LITTLE SIXTEEN

Words and Music
by CHUCK BERRY

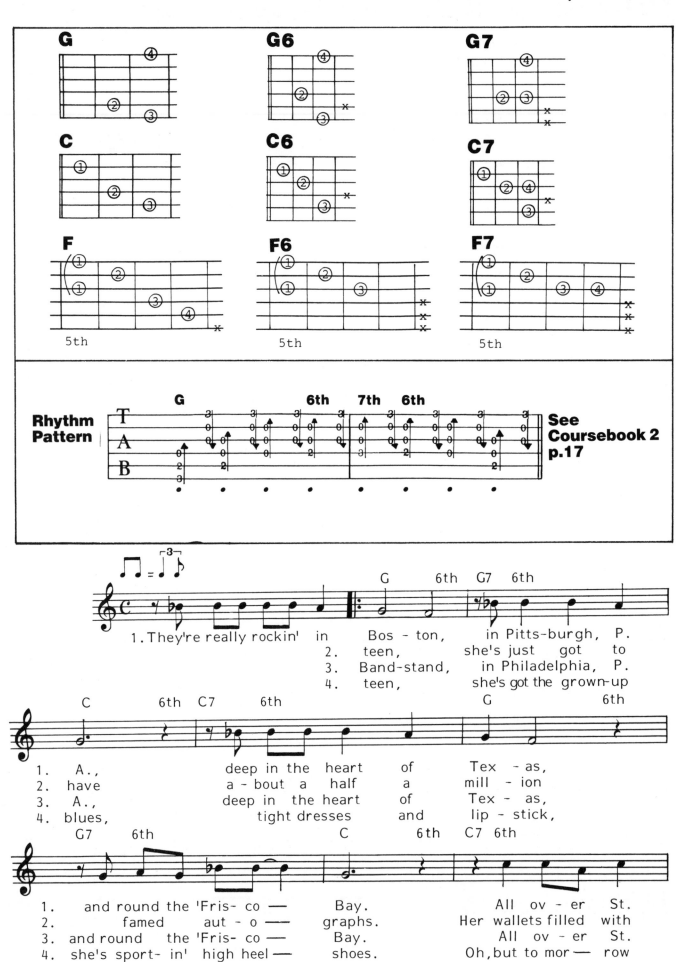

ALL SHOOK UP

Words and Music by
OTIS BLACKWELL and ELVIS PRESLEY

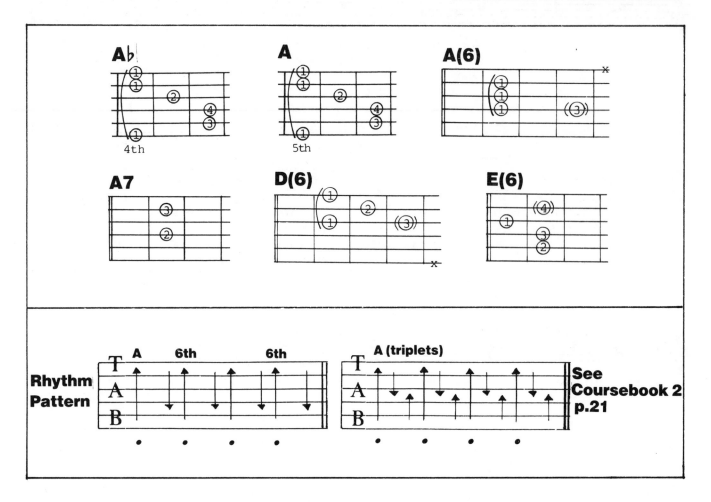

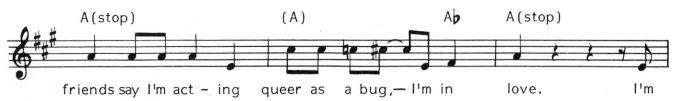

ONLY THE LONELY

Words and Music by
ROY ORBISON and JOE MELSON

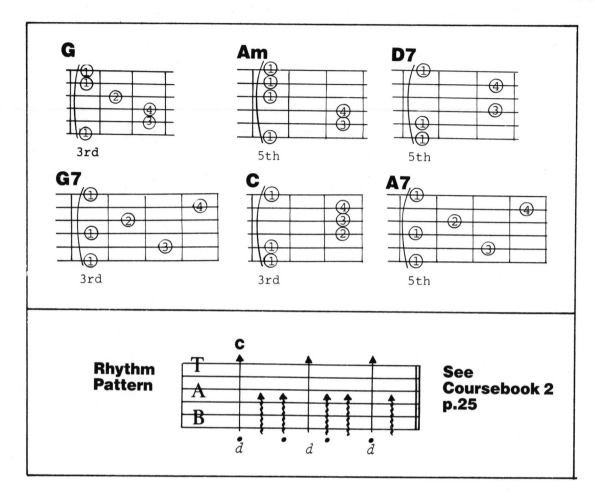

right. There goes— my ba - by.
you. May - be— to - mor - row

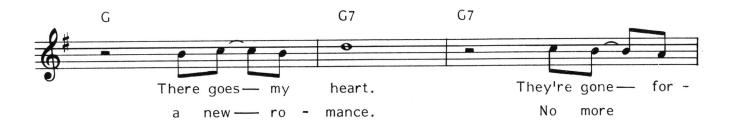

There goes— my heart. They're gone— for -
a new— ro - mance. No more

ev - er. So far— a - part.—
sor - row, but that's— the chance—

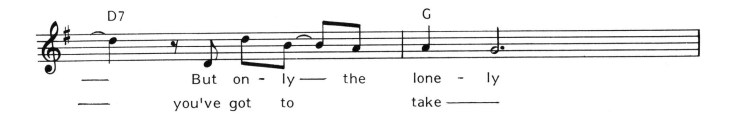

— But on - ly— the lone - ly
— you've got to take—

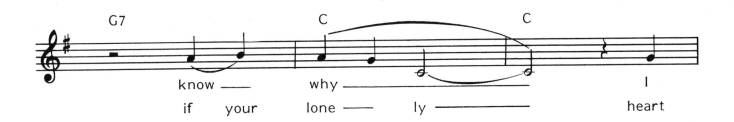

know— why— I
if your lone— ly— heart

cry— on - ly— the lone - ly.
breaks.— On -ly— the lone - ly.

WOMAN

Words and Music
by JOHN LENNON

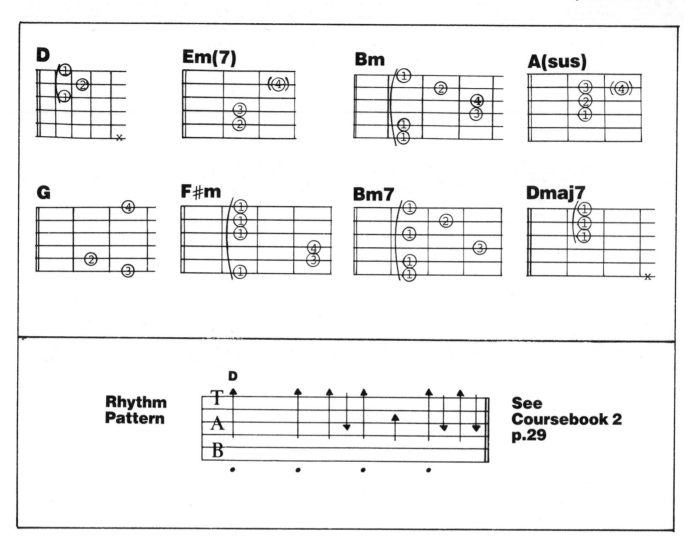

1. Wo - man   I can   hard-ly ex-press
2. Wo - man   I know you   un — der-stand

my mixed e - mo-tions at my   thoughtless-ness.
the lit - tle child   in - side the man.

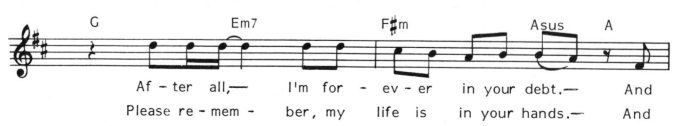

Af - ter all,— I'm for - ev - er in your debt.— And
Please re - mem - ber, my life is in your hands.— And

1. wo~man, I will try to ex-press——
2. wo~man, hold me close to your heart;——
3. wo~man, please let me ex-plain,——

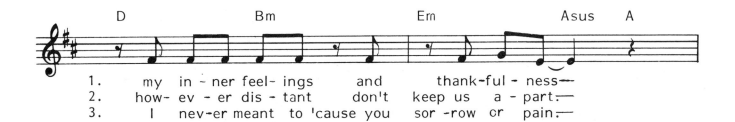

1. my in~ner feel~ings and thank-ful~ness——
2. how~ev~er dis~tant don't keep us a~part.——
3. I nev~er meant to 'cause you sor~row or pain.——

1. for showing me the mean~ing of suc~cess.——
2. Af~ter all, it is writ~ten in the stars.——
3. So let me tell you a~gain and a~gain and a~gain.——

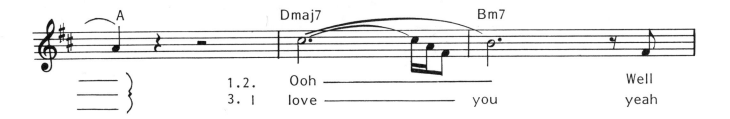

1.2. Ooh —— Well
3. I love —— you yeah

well, doo doo doo doo doo.—— Ooh,——
yeah, now and for~ev~er.—— I love

—— well well, doo doo doo doo doo.——
you. Yeah, yeah, now and for~ev~er.——

PASS THE DUTCHIE

Words and Music by JACKIE MITTOO,
LLOYD FERGUSON and FITZROY SIMPSON

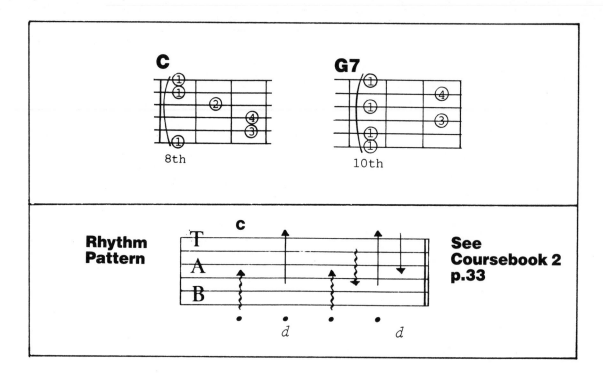

See
Coursebook 2
p.33

CHORUS

Pass —— the dut-chie on the left hand side.

Pass—the dutchie on the left hand side. It gon-na burn. Give me the music, make me

jump and prance. It a go done. Give me the music, make me rock in at the dance. 1. It was a

VERSE

cool and love-ly bree-zy af-ter-noon.——
2. stop to find out what was go-ing on.——

DO YOU FEEL MY LOVE

Words and Music
by EDDY GRANT

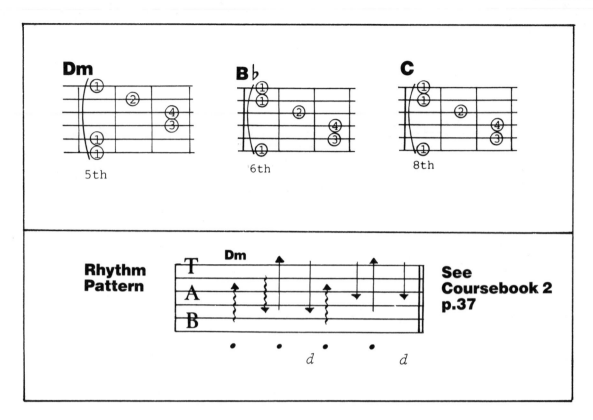

Rhythm Pattern

See Coursebook 2 p.37

You left me with a prob - lem.

Now I know what it's all a-bout.—— You took my heart and

split it up. Now you know what it's all a- bout.—— Do you

CHORUS

feel my love? Do you feel it as I

walk a - way? —— Do you feel my love?

Do you feel it as I walk a - way?—

MIDDLE SECTION

Need to find my-self. All —— that I've got left.

Used up, oh I'm used up. Need —— to cry, but still. Got—

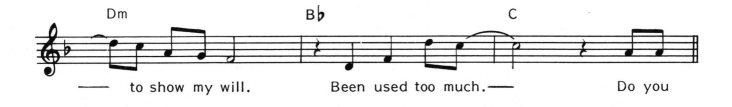

—— to show my will. Been used too much. —— Do you

HAPPY MUSIC

Words and Music
by RUSS SHIPTON

Rhythm Pattern

See Coursebook 2 p.41

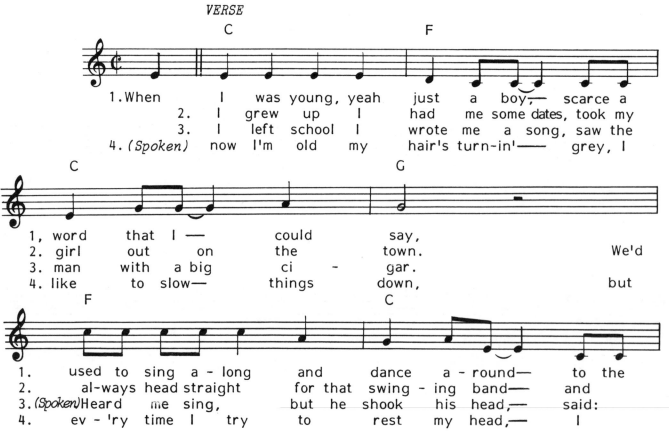

VERSE

C   **F**

1.When   I   was young, yeah   just   a   boy,—   scarce a
   2.   I   grew   up   I   had   me some dates, took my
   3.   I   left school I   wrote   me   a song, saw the
      4.(Spoken)   now I'm old   my   hair's turn-in'——   grey, I

C   **G**

1, word   that I —   could   say,
2. girl   out   on   the   town.   We'd
3. man   with   a big   ci - gar.
4. like   to slow—   things   down,   but

F   **C**

1.   used to sing a - long   and   dance a - round—   to the
2.   al-ways head straight   for that   swing - ing band—   and
3.(Spoken)Heard   me sing,   but he shook   his head,—   said:
4.   ev - 'ry time I try   to   rest   my head,—   I

© 1986 Russ Shipton

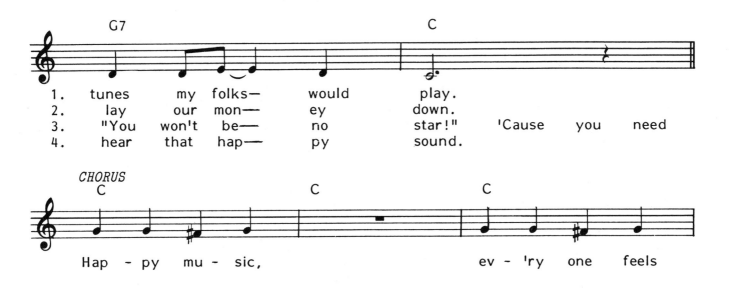

1. tunes my folks— would play.
2. lay our mon— ey down.
3. "You won't be— no star!" 'Cause you need
4. hear that hap— py sound.

CHORUS

Hap - py mu - sic, ev - 'ry one feels

fine, with a jump - in' beat, and a

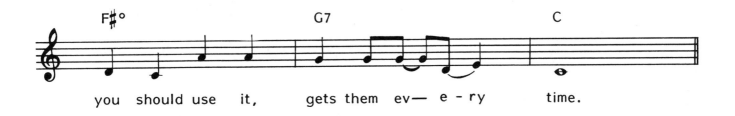

sim - ple rhyme. Hap - py mus - ic,

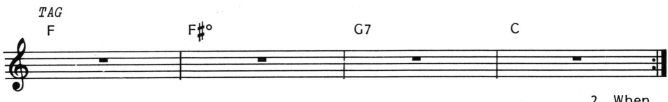

you should use it, gets them ev— e - ry time.

TAG

F   F#°   G7   C

2. When
3. When
4. Well,

EASY LOVIN'

Words and Music
by RUSS SHIPTON

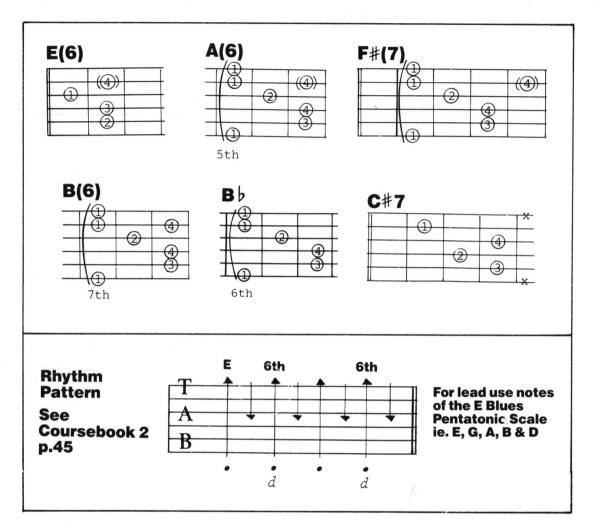

Rhythm Pattern

See Coursebook 2 p.45

For lead use notes of the E Blues Pentatonic Scale ie. E, G, A, B & D

VERSE

1. Rest - less nights— with - out you there,—
2. No - one out— there seems to know—

While you're won-d'rin— if I — care.— What-ev-er hap-pened—
why good lov- in' can come and— go.— What-ev-er hap-pened—

to those— days;— when we were— wild— and free?
to that— spar— kle that we once— had— be - fore?

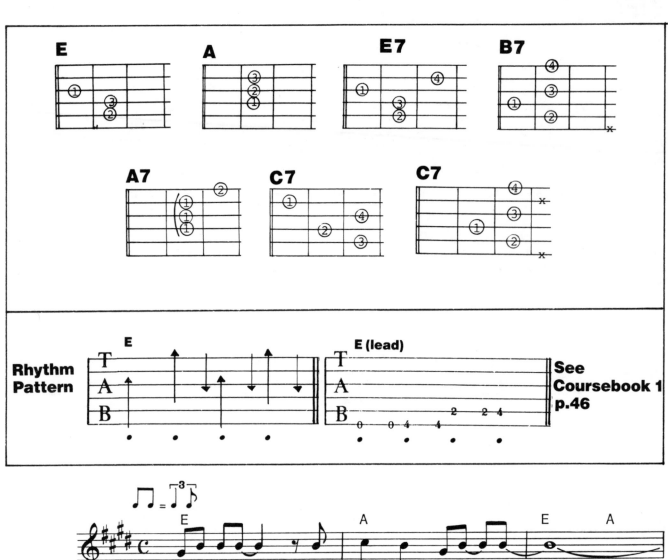

LEAD ME ANYWHERE

48

Words and Music
by RUSS SHIPTON

Rhythm Pattern

See Coursebook 1 p.46

© 1986 Russ Shipton

4/86

RUSS SHIPTON'S Rock & Pop Guitar Songbook 4

Note: The songs in this book provide more practice material for "Russ Shiptons Rock & Pop Guitar" course. References are given to guitar styles and techniques covered in coursebooks 3 & 4 which can be used to play these additional songs.

First Published 1986
© International Music Publications

Exclusive Distributors
International Music Publications
Southend Road, Woodford Green,
Essex IG8 8HN, England.

Printed in England by JB Offset (Marks Tey) Limited
Marks Tey, Essex.

I ONLY WANT TO BE WITH YOU

Words and Music by
MIKE HAWKER and IVOR RAYMONDE

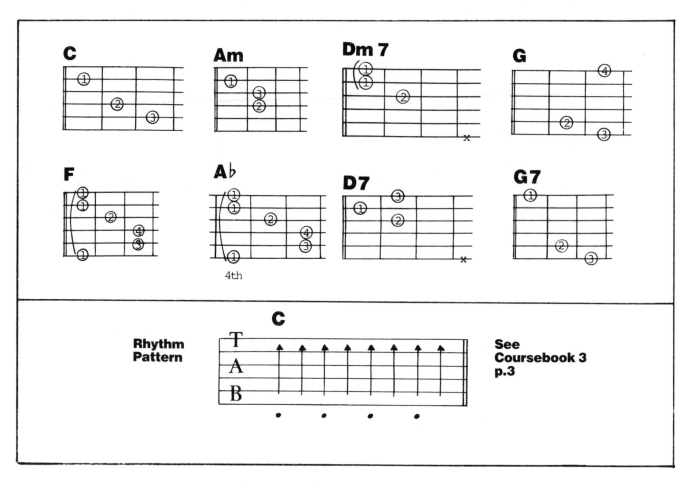

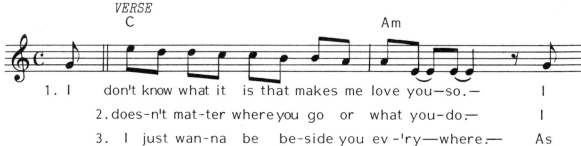

ev - er since we met you've had a hold on— me?— It
nev - er knew that I could be in love like — this.— It's
ev - er since we met you've had a hold on — me?— No

hap - pens to be— true,— I on-ly want to be with— you.—
cra - zy but it's— true,— I on-ly want to be with — you.—
mat - ter what you — do,— I on-ly want to be with — you.—

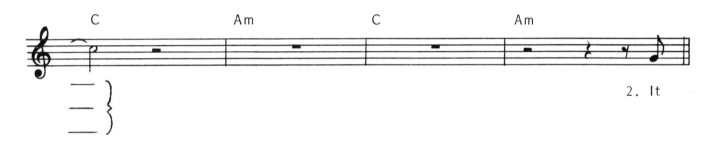

2. It

MIDDLE SECTION

You stopped and smiled at me,— asked me if I'd care to

dance.— I fell in-to your op-en— arms.—

I did-n't stand a — chance.— 3.Now lis -ten, hon-ey,

WHEREVER I LAY MY HAT (That's My Home)

Words and Music by MARVIN GAYE,
NORMAN WHITFIELD and BARRETT STRONG

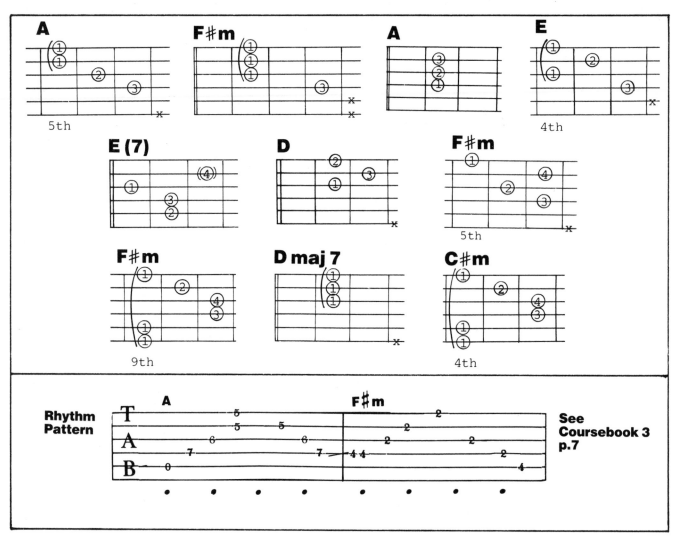

VERSE

A(5th pos)

1. By the look in your eye, I can
2. had a ro - mance, did you
3. I'm the type of guy who

F#m   A

tell you're gon - na cry.   Is it ov - er me?—
break it by chance   ov - er me?————
gives a girl the eye,   ev - 'ry - bo - dy knows.—

E(4th Pos)   A(5th Pos)

If it is save your tears,—   for
If it's so I'd like for you to know that
But I love them and I leave them, break their

5

PROUD MARY

Words and Music
by J C FOGERTY

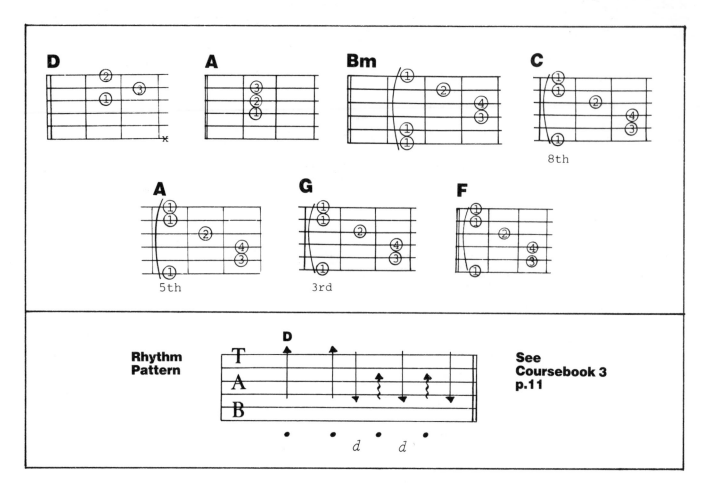

See
Coursebook 3
p.11

VERSE

1. Left a good job— in the ci-ty,—
2. Cleaned a lot of plates in Mem-phis,—
3. If you come down to the riv-er,—

work-ing for the man ev-'ry night and— day,—
Pumped a lot of pain down in New Or—leans.—
bet you gon-na find some peo-ple who live.—

and I nev-er lost one min-ute of sleep-ing,
But I nev-er saw the good side of the city, un-
You don't have to worry, 'cause you have no money.

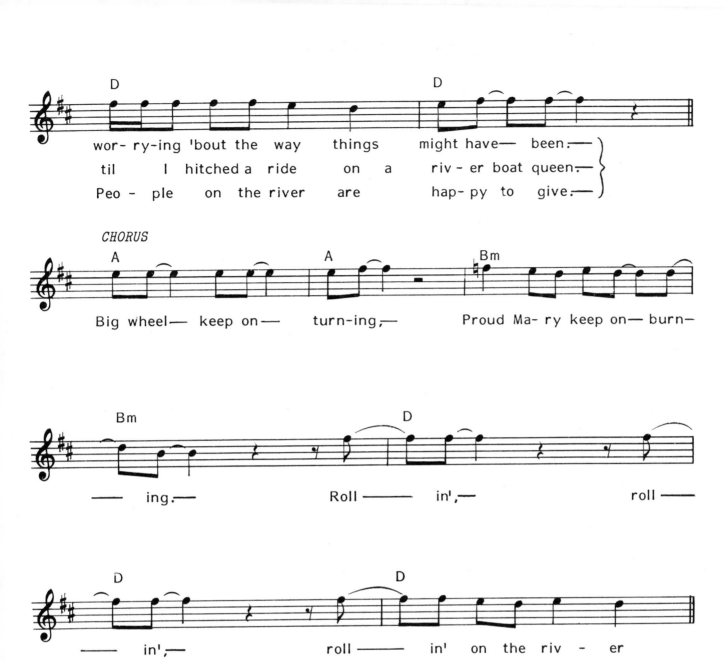

wor- ry-ing 'bout the way   things   might have— been.—
til   I   hitched a   ride   on   a   riv- er boat queen.—
Peo - ple   on   the river   are   hap-py to give.—

CHORUS

Big wheel— keep on— turn-ing,—   Proud Ma- ry keep on— burn—

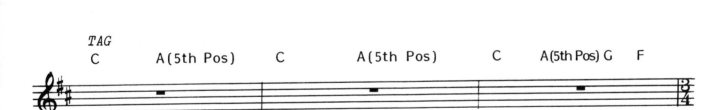

— ing.—   Roll — in',—   roll —

— in';—   roll — in' on the riv - er

TAG

C   A(5th Pos)   C   A(5th Pos)   C   A(5th Pos) G   F

F   D   D

EASY LIFE

Words and Music
by RUSS SHIPTON

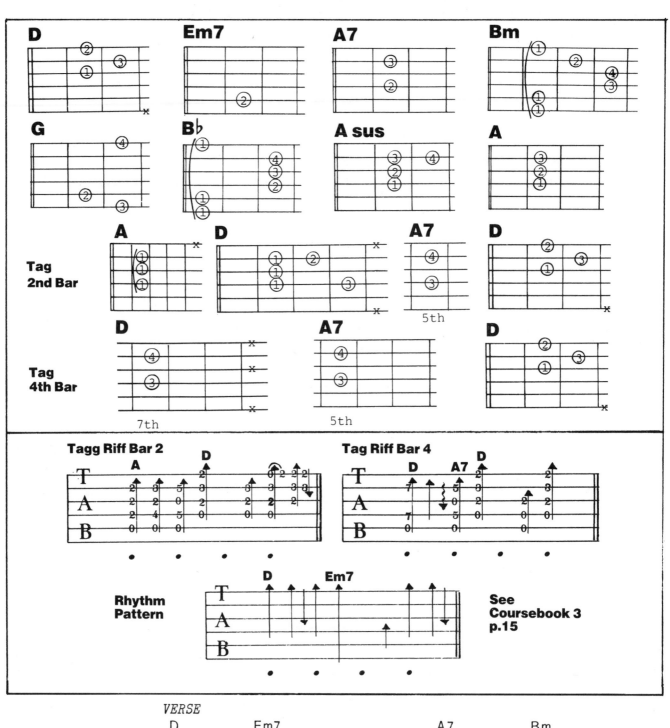

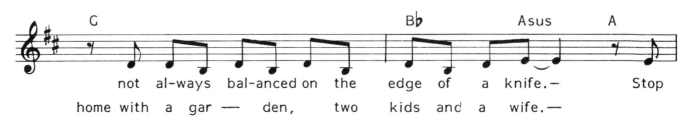

play- ing the clown,— put my feet on the ground.—
My head is sore,— but I know the cure —

I like the sound of an ea - sy life.—
is noth-ing more than an ea - sy life.—

TAG

MIDDLE SECTION

Now to some guys— it may come ea - sy,— take a

girl and— set - tle down. But

cra - zy — cats — who've bin mov - in' so fast— find it

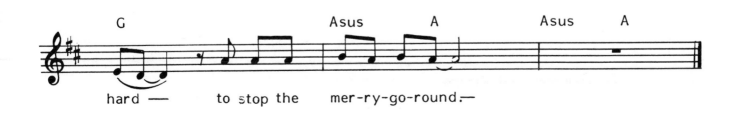

hard — to stop the mer-ry-go-round.—

LOVE OF THE COMMON PEOPLE

Words and Music by
JOHN HURLEY and RONNIE WILKINS

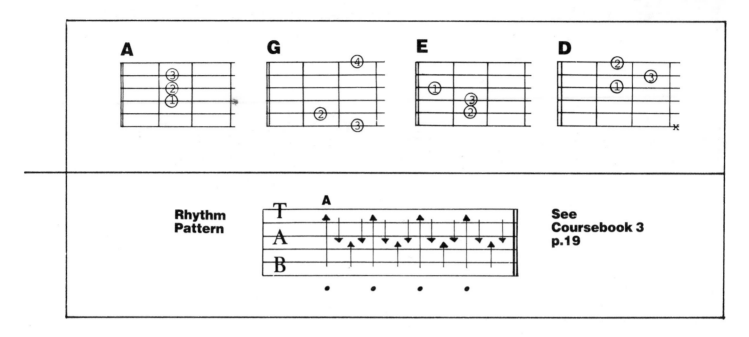

VERSE 1

A

Liv - in' on free food tick - ets ———

wa-ter in the milk from a hole in the roof where the rain came through, what can you

do? —————— Tears from the lit- tle sis- ter,

cry-ing 'cause she doesn't have a dress without a patch for the party to go, but you

Sub-published by EMI Music Publishing Ltd, London WC2H 0LD/Westminster Music Ltd, 19/20 Poland Street, London W1

CHORUS

know she'll get by, 'cause she's liv-in' in the love of the common peo—ple,

smiles from the heart of a fa-mi-ly man.— Dad-dy's gon-na buy you a dream to cling— to,

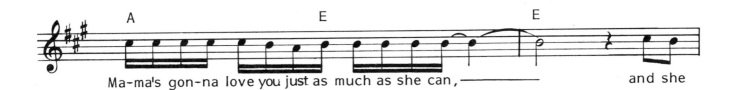

Ma-ma's gon-na love you just as much as she can,————— and she

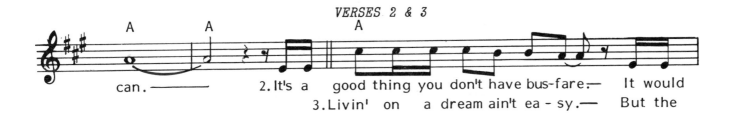

VERSES 2 & 3

can.——— 2.It's a good thing you don't have bus-fare.— It would
3.Livin' on a dream ain't ea-sy.— But the

fall through the hole in your pock-et and you'd lose it in the
clo - ser the knit, the tight— er the fit and the

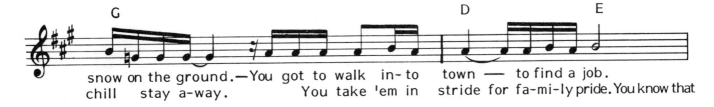

snow on the ground.—You got to walk in-to town — to find a job.
chill stay a-way. You take 'em in stride for fa-mi-ly pride. You know that

Try-in' to keep your hands warm,—when the hole in your shoe lets the snow come through and chills
faith is in your founda-tion, and with a whole lot of love and a warm conversation but

— you to the bone. Now you'd better go home where it's warm—Where you can
don't for-get to pray. Making it strong where you be-long, and we're

HIS LATEST FLAME

Words and Music by
DOC POMUS and MORT SHUMAN

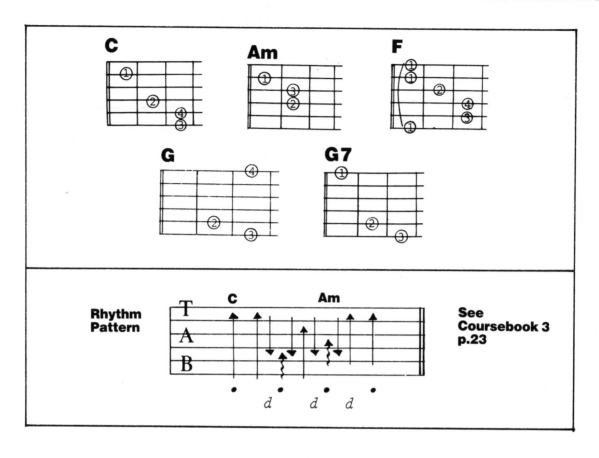

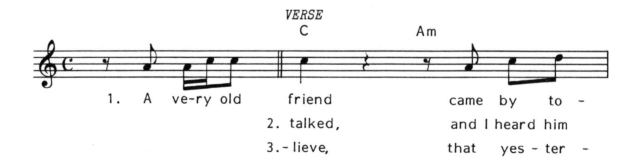

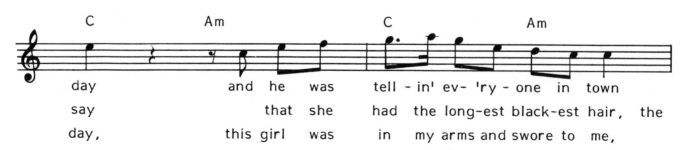

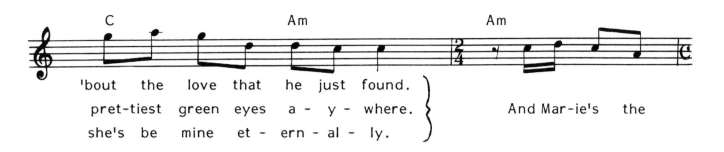

'bout the love that he just found.
pret-tiest green eyes a - y - where.
she's be mine et - ern - al - ly.

And Mar-ie's the

name   of his lat-est   flame.   2. He talked and

MIDDLE SECTION

Though I smiled, the tears in- side were a - burn-in'.—   I

wished him luck and then he said good - bye.

He   was gone, but still   his words kept re - turn- in'.—   What

else was there for me to do— but   cry?   3. Would you be-

SECOND HAND NEWS

Words and Music
by LINDSEY BUCKINGHAM

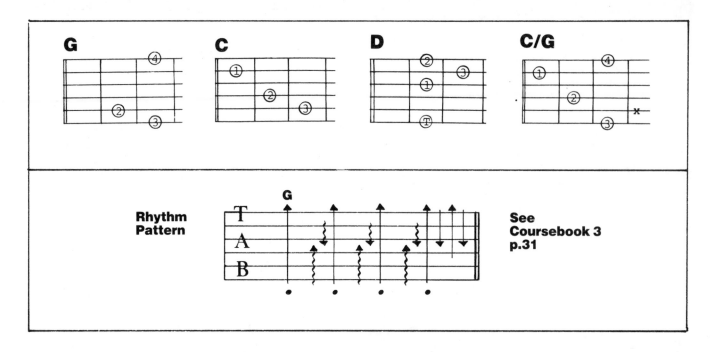

Rhythm Pattern

See Coursebook 3 p.31

VERSE

1. I know there's noth-ing to say.—
2. One thing I think you should know:—

Some- one has tak - en my place.— When
I ain't gonna miss you when you go.— Been

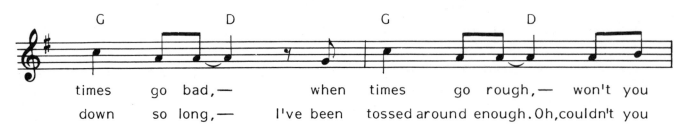

times go bad,— when times go rough,— won't you
down so long,— I've been tossed around enough. Oh, couldn't you

lay me down— in the tall grass and let me do— my stuff.——
just let me— go down and let me do— my stuff.——

I know I got nothin' on you— I know there's
I know you're hopin' to find— Some-one who's gonna give you

noth-in'—— to do. When times go bad— and you
peace of —— mind.— When times go bad, when

can't get e-nough,— won't you lay me down—in the tall grass and
times go rough,— won't you lay me down—in the tall grass and

TAG

let me do — my stuff.——
let me do — my stuff.——

Boum,—boum boum, boum,— boum.

Boum,—boum boum,boum,— boum.

Boum,— boum boum,boum,— boum,

ENDING

boum,boum,boum,boum.—

I'm— just sec-ond-hand

news, I'm— just sec-ond-hand news.

YOU SHOULD BE DANCING

Words and Music by
BARRY, ROBIN and MAURICE GIBB

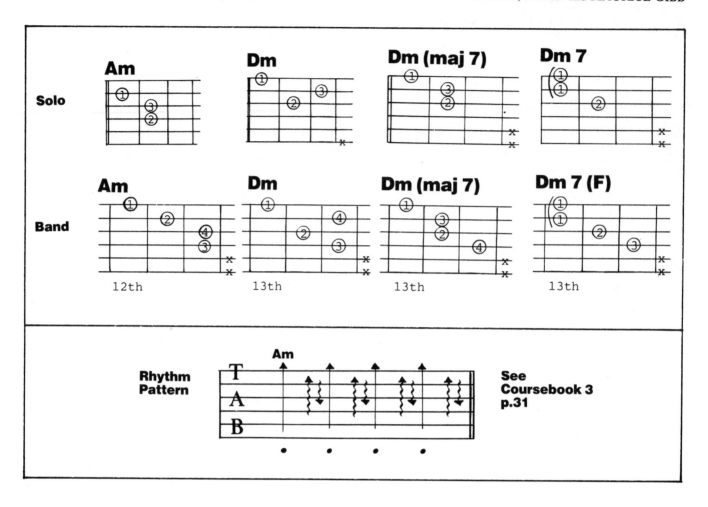

1. My ba- by moves—at mid-night,— goes

2. jui- cy and—she's trou-ble.—— She

right on till the dawn.— My

gets it to me good.— My

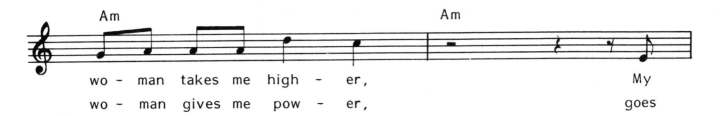

wo - man takes me high - er,
wo - man gives me pow - er,

My
goes

wo - man keeps— me warm.—
right down to — my blood.—

What you

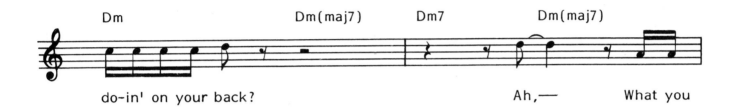

do-in' on your back?

Ah,— What you

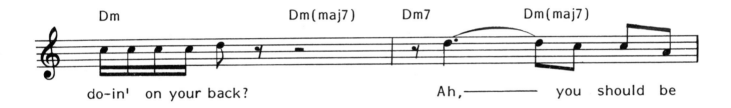

do-in' on your back?

Ah,——— you should be

danc ——— in' ——— yeah,———

danc ——— in',——— yeah. ———

2. She's

GET DOWN ON IT

Words and Music by RONALD BELL,
JAMES TAYLOR and KOOL AND THE GANG

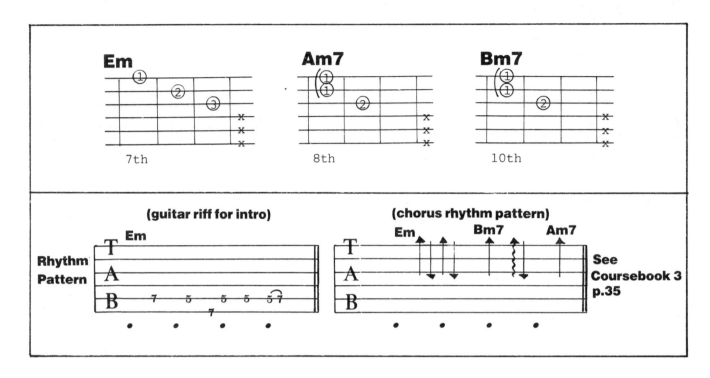

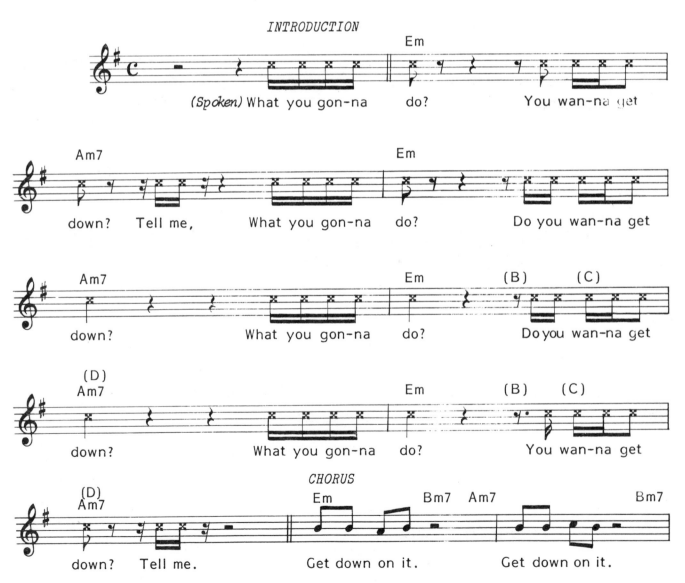

EYE OF THE TIGER

Words and Music by
FRANKIE SULLIVAN II and JIM PETERIK

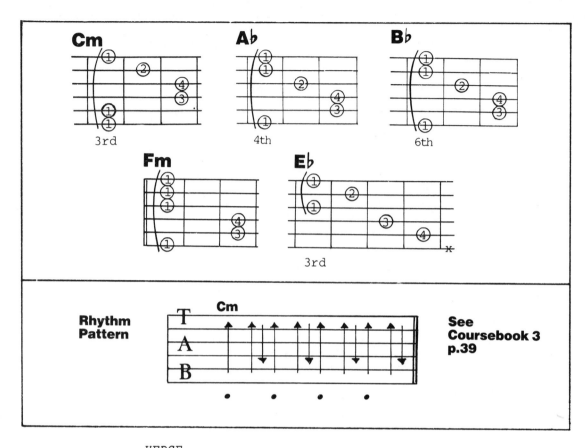

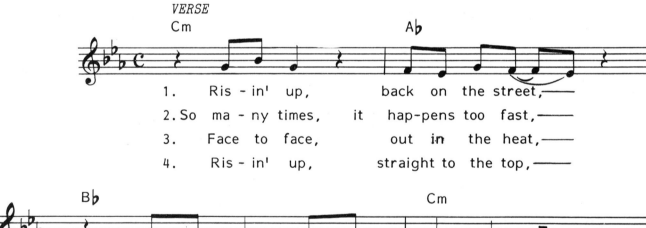

VERSE

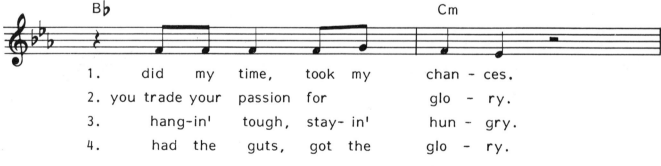

1. Ris - in' up,   back on the street,———
2. So ma - ny times,   it hap-pens too fast,———
3. Face to face,   out in the heat,———
4. Ris - in' up,   straight to the top,———

1. did my time, took my   chan - ces.
2. you trade your passion for   glo - ry.
3. hang-in' tough, stay-in'   hun - gry.
4. had the guts, got the   glo - ry.

1. Went the dis-tance, now I'm   back on   my feet, just a
2. Don't lose your grip   on the   dreams of the past, you must
3. They stack the odds,   still we   take to the street, for the
4. Went the dis-tance, now I'm   not gon - na stop, just a

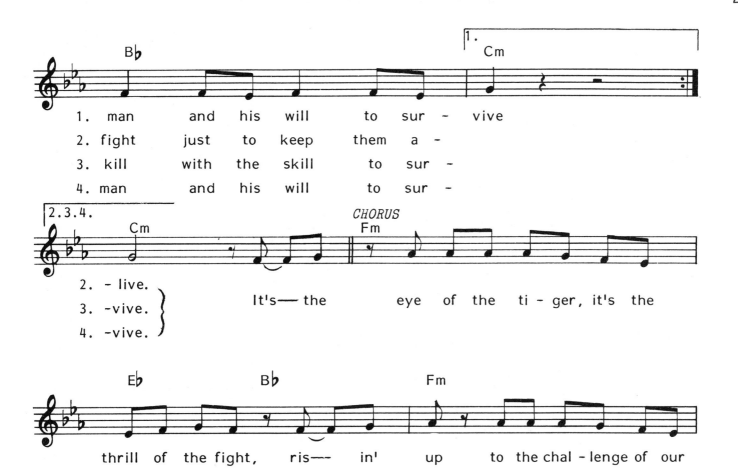

1. man   and   his   will   to   sur - vive
2. fight   just   to   keep   them   a -
3. kill   with   the   skill   to   sur -
4. man   and   his   will   to   sur -

2. - live.
3. -vive.
4. -vive.

CHORUS

It's— the   eye   of   the   ti - ger, it's the

thrill   of   the   fight,   ris— in'   up   to   the   chal - lenge of our

ri — val.   And—   the   last   known sur-vi - vor stalks his

prey   in   the   night,   and—   he's   watch-in'   us   all   with   the

eye   of   the   ti — ger.

MAYBE TOMORROW

Words and Music
by RUSS SHIPTON

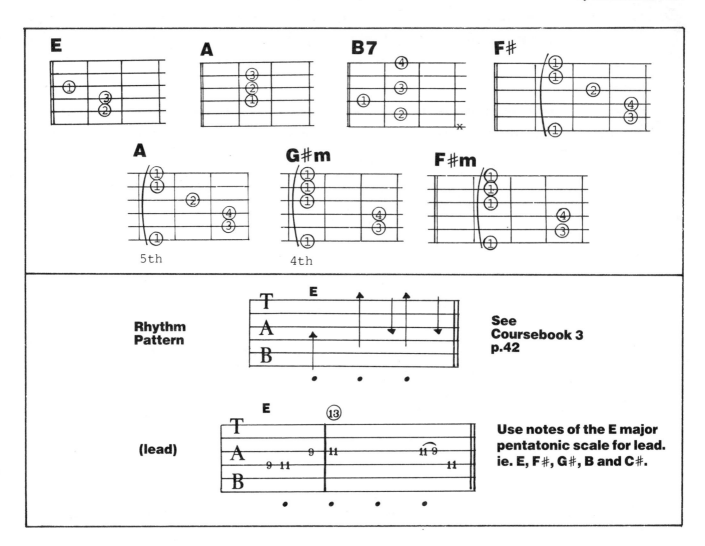

E   A   B7   F#

A (5th)   G#m (4th)   F#m

Rhythm
Pattern

See
Coursebook 3
p.42

(lead)

Use notes of the E major
pentatonic scale for lead.
ie. E, F#, G#, B and C#.

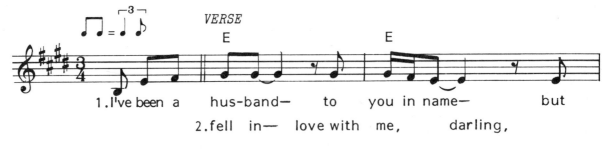

VERSE

E ... E

1. I've been a hus-band— to you in name— but
2. fell in— love with me, darling,

A ... E ... E

not it — re-a-li-ty. Still you've loved me— just the
all those— years a-go, how could you fore-see what

E ... B7 ... B7

same,— and al-ways— stuck by me, through the
time would bring, how could you know that I'd

THE YOUNG AT HEART

Words and Music
by RUSS SHIPTON

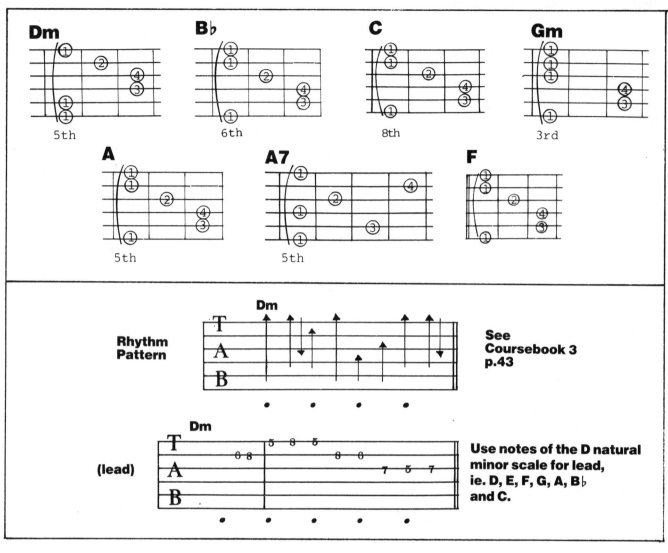

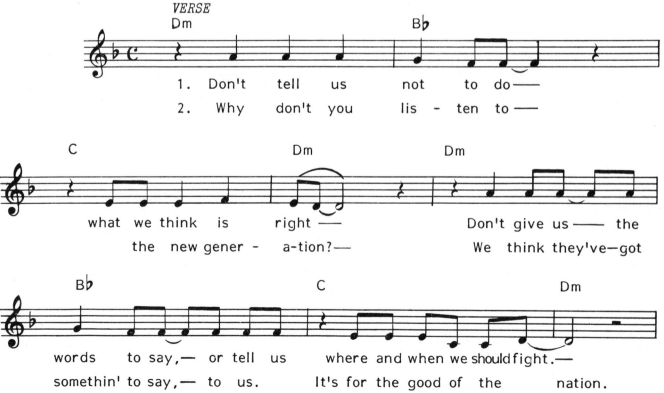

Gm   Dm

You think — your world is fine. —
Their fu — ture's in your hands; —

C   Dm   Dm

You think— you know it all.—   But we're the
don't think you know it all.—   Join those who're

Gm   A   A7

young at heart, —   and we've heard — the
young at heart, —   who have heard — the

CHORUS

Dm   F   C

call.— So we'll } do what we have to do, —
call.— And we'll }

Dm   C   B♭

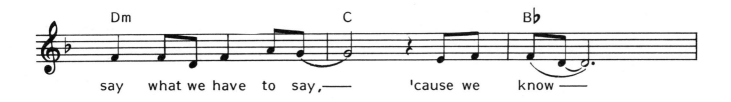

say what we have to say, — 'cause we know —

A (stop)   Dm   Dm

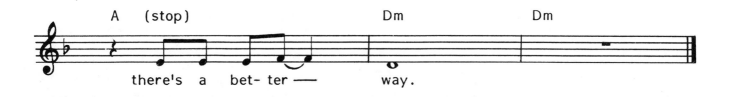

there's a bet- ter — way.

YOU'RE SO VAIN

Words and Music
by CARYL SIMON

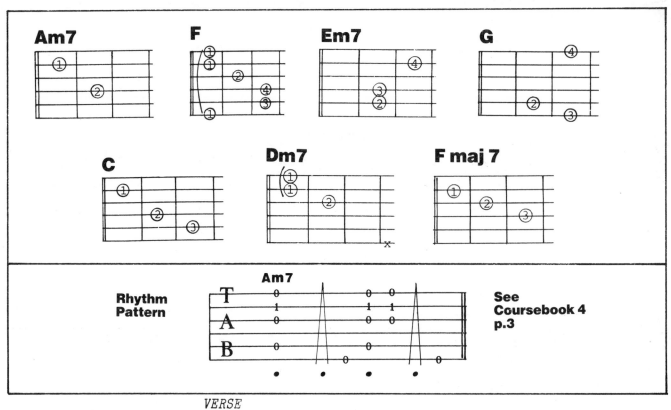

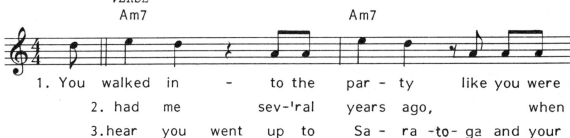

VERSE

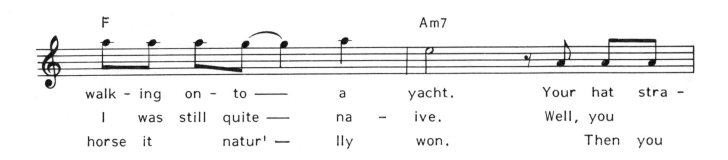

1. You walked in - to the par - ty like you were
2. had me sev-'ral years ago, when
3. hear you went up to Sa - ra -to- ga and your

walk - ing on - to —— a yacht. Your hat stra -
I was still quite —— na - ive. Well, you
horse it natur' — lly won. Then you

teg - ic - 'lly dipped —— be - low one eye —— Your
said that we made such a pret - ty pair,—— and
flew your Lear jet up to No - va Scotia, to see the

© 1972 & 1986 Quackenbush Music Ltd
Warner Bros Music Ltd, 17 Berners Street, London W1P 3DD

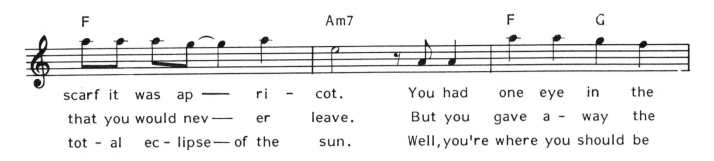

scarf it was ap — ri - cot. You had one eye in the
that you would nev — er leave. But you gave a - way the
tot - al ec - lipse — of the sun. Well, you're where you should be

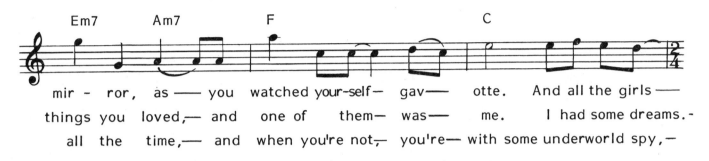

mir - ror, as — you watched your-self — gav — otte. And all the girls —
things you loved,— and one of them — was — me. I had some dreams. -
all the time,— and when you're not, — you're — with some underworld spy, —

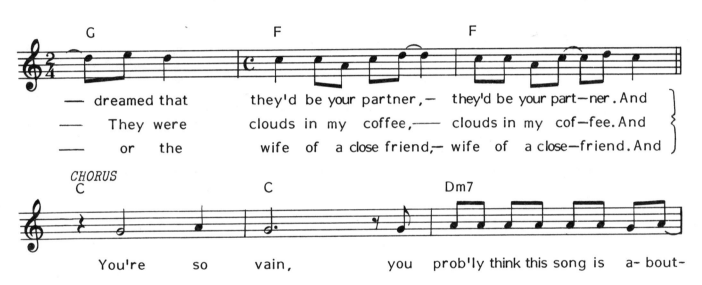

— dreamed that they'd be your partner, — they'd be your part—ner. And
— They were clouds in my coffee, —— clouds in my cof—fee. And
— or the wife of a close friend, — wife of a close—friend. And

CHORUS

You're so vain, you prob'ly think this song is a-bout-

— you. You're so vain, I bet you think this song is a-bout —

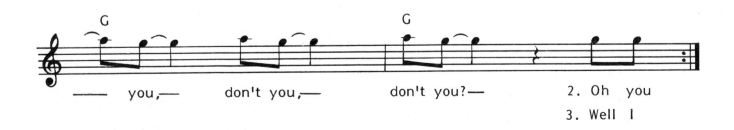

— you,— don't you,— don't you?— 2. Oh you
3. Well I

HOW CAN YOU MEND A BROKEN HEART

Words and Music by
BARRY GIBB and ROBIN GIBB

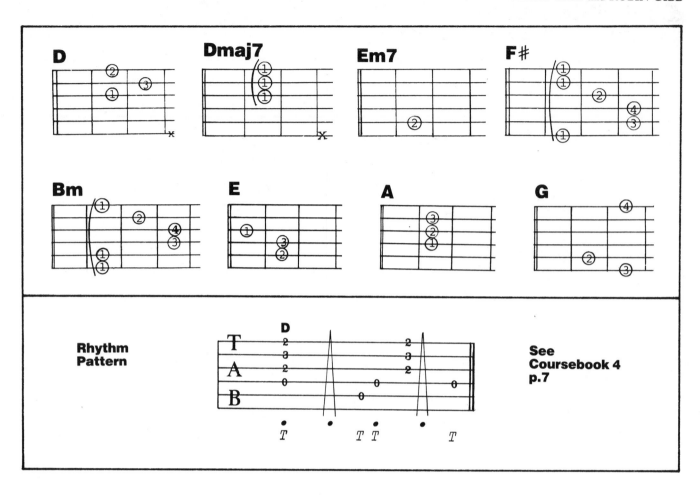

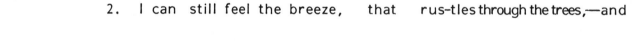

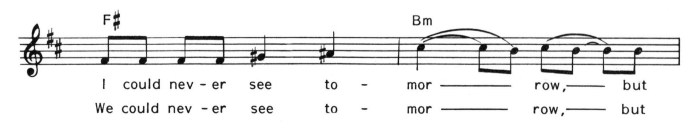

WONDERFUL TONIGHT

Words and Music
by ERIC CLAPTON

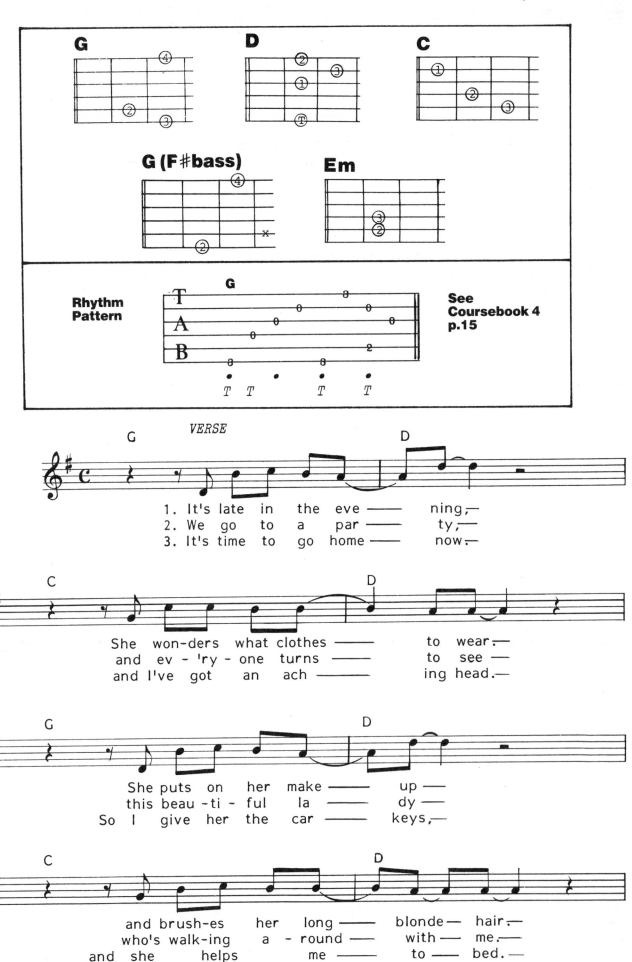

Rhythm Pattern

See Coursebook 4 p.15

VERSE

1. It's late in the eve — ning,
2. We go to a par — ty,
3. It's time to go home — now,

She won-ders what clothes — to wear,
and ev-'ry-one turns — to see
and I've got an ach — ing head.

She puts on her make — up —
this beau-ti-ful la — dy —
So I give her the car — keys,

and brush-es her long — blonde — hair.
who's walk-ing a - round — with — me.
and she helps me — to — bed.

MAN OF THE WORLD

Words and Music
by PETER A GREEN

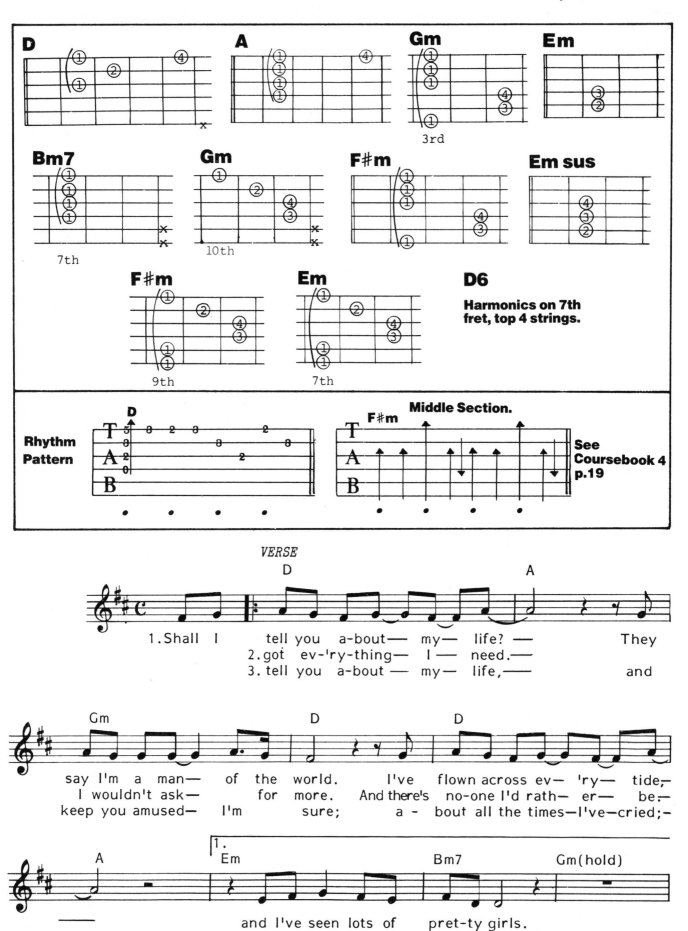

© 1970 & 1986 Clifford David Management Ltd
Assigned to Rachel Music Ltd
Administered by Leosong C.S. Ltd, London W1 for the World

NIGHT FEVER

Words and Music by
BARRY, ROBIN and MAURICE GIBB

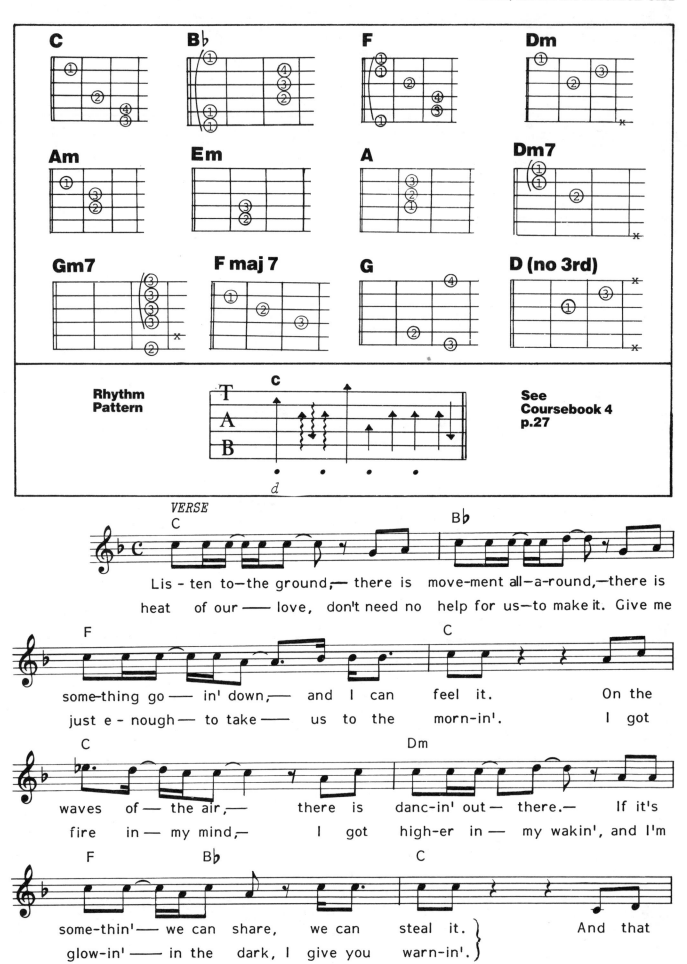

I GOT YOU, BABE

Words and Music
by SONNY BONO

MIDDLE SECTION

flow-ers— in the Spring. I got you, to wear my ring. And when I'm

sad, you're a clown, and if I get scared, you're always a-

round. ——————————— And then they say your hair's too long, but

VERSE 3

I don't care, with you I can't go wrong. Then

put your lit - tle hand in mine, there ain't no hill or mountain we can't

climb, babe. I got you, babe. I got you, babe.

ENDING

I got you to hold my hand.

I got you to under-stand.— I got you to walk with me. I got you to talk with me.

I got you to kiss good-night. I got you to hold me tight.— I got you, I won't let go.

I got you who loves me so. I got you, babe.

DIANA

Words and Music
by PAUL ANKA

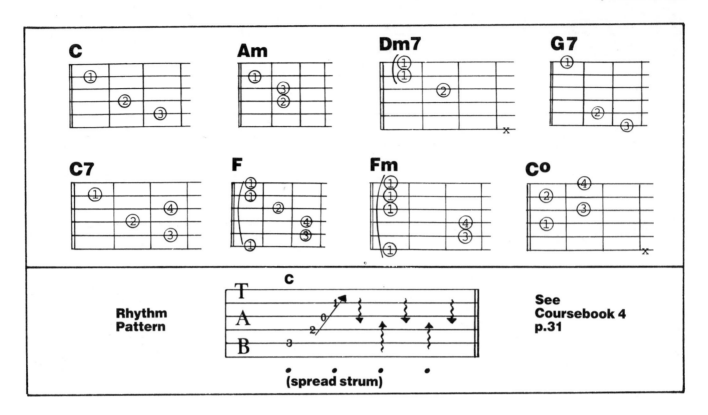

See Coursebook 4 p.31

VERSE

1. I'm so young and you're so old.
2. Thrills I get when you hold me close.
3. On - ly you can take my heart.

This, my dar - ling, I've been told. I don't care just
Oh, my dar - ling, you're the most. I love you, but do
On - ly you can tear it a - part. When you hold me in your

what they say, 'cause for - ev - er I will pray
you love me? Oh, Di - an - a. can't you see?
lov - ing arms, I can feel you giving all your charms.

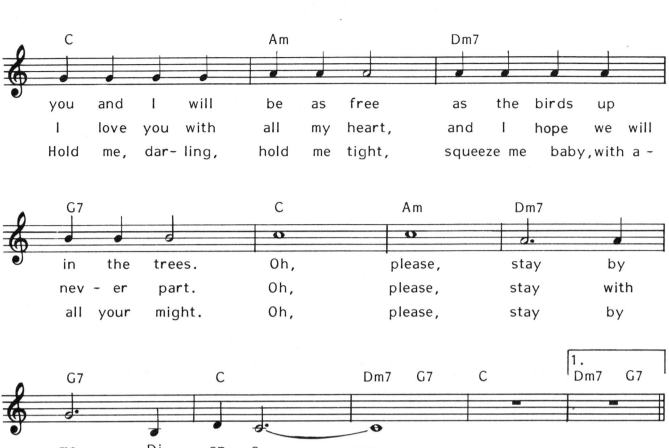

you and I will be as free as the birds up
I love you with all my heart, and I hope we will
Hold me, dar-ling, hold me tight, squeeze me baby, with a -

in the trees. Oh, please, stay by
nev - er part. Oh, please, stay with
all your might. Oh, please, stay by

me, Di - an - a. ————————
me, Di - an - a. ————————
me, Di - an - a. ————————

MIDDLE SECTION

Oh,— my dar-ling,— oh,— my lov - er,—

tell—me that there is— no oth-er.— I— love you

with—my heart. Oh oh, oh oh, oh - oh.————————

SO RIGHT

Words and Music
by RUSS SHIPTON

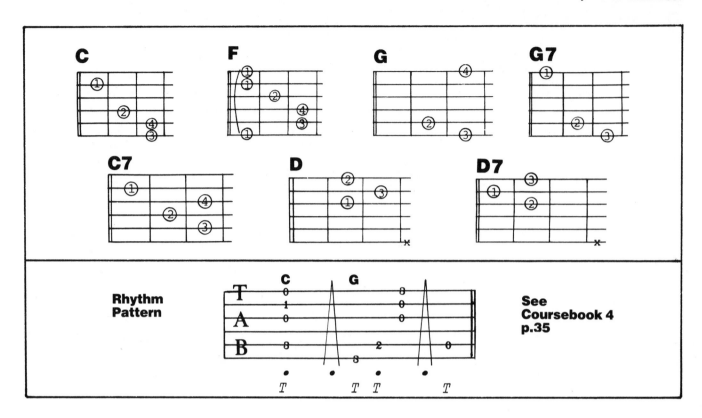

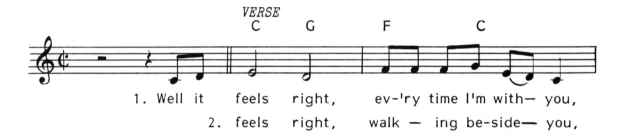

VERSE

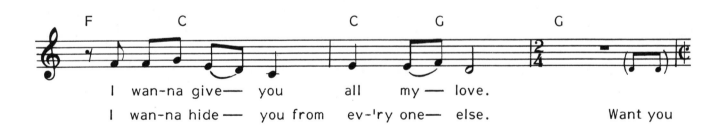

1. Well it feels right, ev-'ry time I'm with— you,
2. feels right, walk — ing be-side— you,

I wan-na give— you all my — love.
I wan-na hide— you from ev-'ry one— else. Want you

Day and night, ev - er since I found — you, I
for my - self. Ev - er since I saw — you, I

wan - na be a - round—— you, hold you tight,
could not ig - nore—— you, please hold me tight,

it feels— so— right.——
it feels— so— right.——

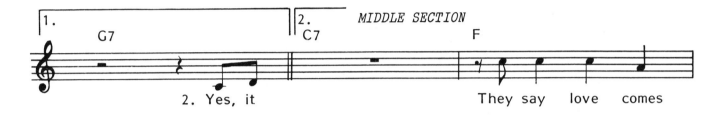

1.　G7　　　　　2.　C7　　MIDDLE SECTION　　F

2. Yes, it　　　　　　　　　They say love comes

F　　　　　　　　　　　C

once in a life—— time.——　　Well, then,——

C　　　　　D　　　　　D7

this must be my— time.——　You've been— so　good for me.——

G　　　　　　　　　　G7　　　　(Rpt. Vs 1)

May - be some things—— are —— meant to — be, 'cause it

LIGHT THE CANDLE

Words and Music
by RUSS SHIPTON

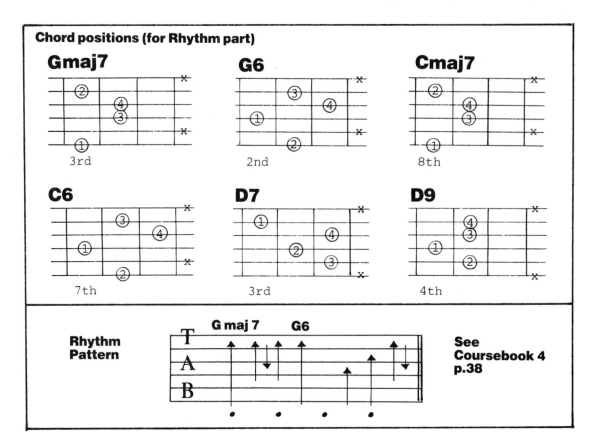

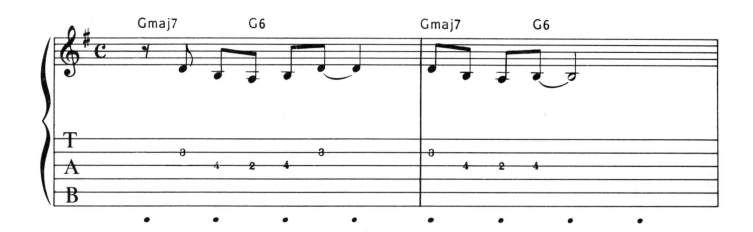

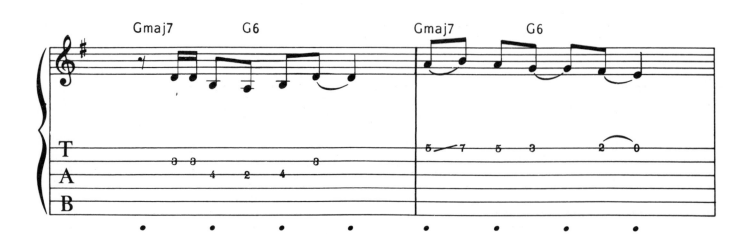

CAROL

Words and Music
by CHUCK BERRY

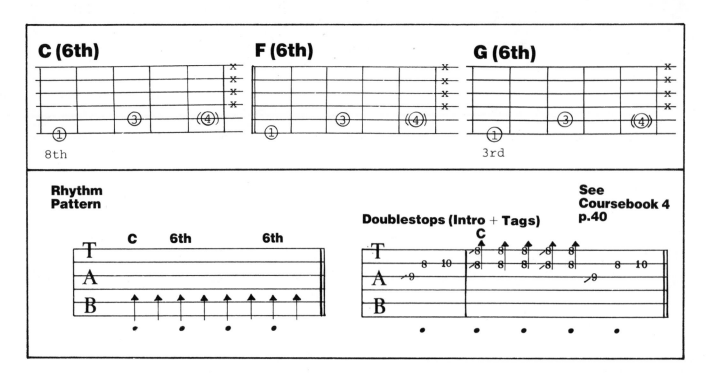

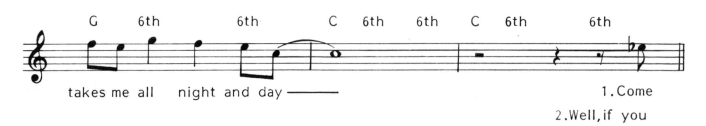

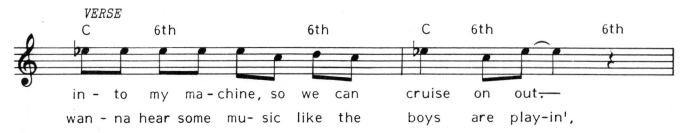

KILLER ON THE LOOSE

Words and Music
by PHIL LYNOTT

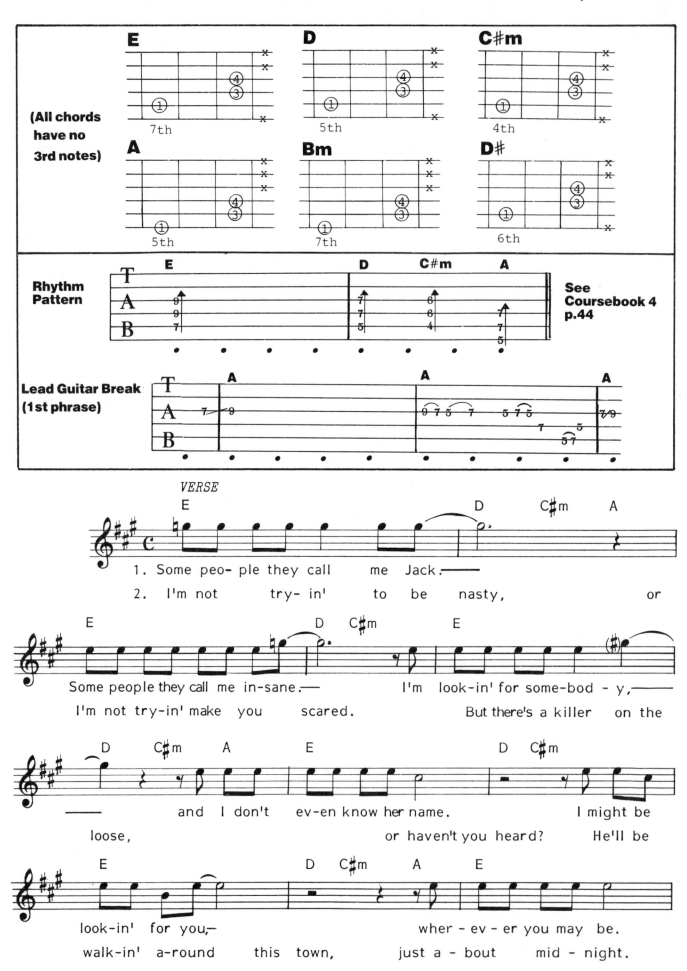

See Coursebook 4 p.44

VERSE

1. Some peo-ple they call me Jack.—
2. I'm not try-in' to be nasty, or

Some people they call me in-sane.— I'm look-in' for some-bod-y,—
I'm not try-in' make you scared. But there's a killer on the

and I don't ev-en know her name. I might be
loose, or haven't you heard? He'll be

look-in' for you,— wher-ev-er you may be.
walk-in' a-round this town, just a-bout mid-night.

For there's some-thin' I've got to do for you hon-ey,— and it's be -
Yes,   that's Chi-na - town,

tween you and me.   Now you might—think it's fun;—— or
That's right, that's right.   Now you might—think I'm messing,

may - be it's a joke.——   But you've got plenty reason to wor—
or he don't ex ——— ist.   But honey,

— ry, hon-ey,—   'cause you would-n't stand a hope. There's a kill-er on the
I'm confessing,   I'm a need sex - u- al rap-
(There's a kill-er on the)

CHORUS

loose a-gain.——   A kill-er on the loose.   There's a
(2. ist.)

kill-er on the loose a-gain.——   A la-dy kill-er on the loose, ah.   2. Now

MIDDLE SECTION

——— 24 bars A chord ———

(Spoken) I'll be standing in the shadows of love, waiting for you.
Don't unzip your zipper, 'cause you know I'm Jack the Ripper.
Now don't wait, don't ....

BREAK

——— 16 bars A chord ———   ——— 8 bars Bm chord ———

SWEET WOMAN OF MINE

Words and Music
by RUSS SHIPTON

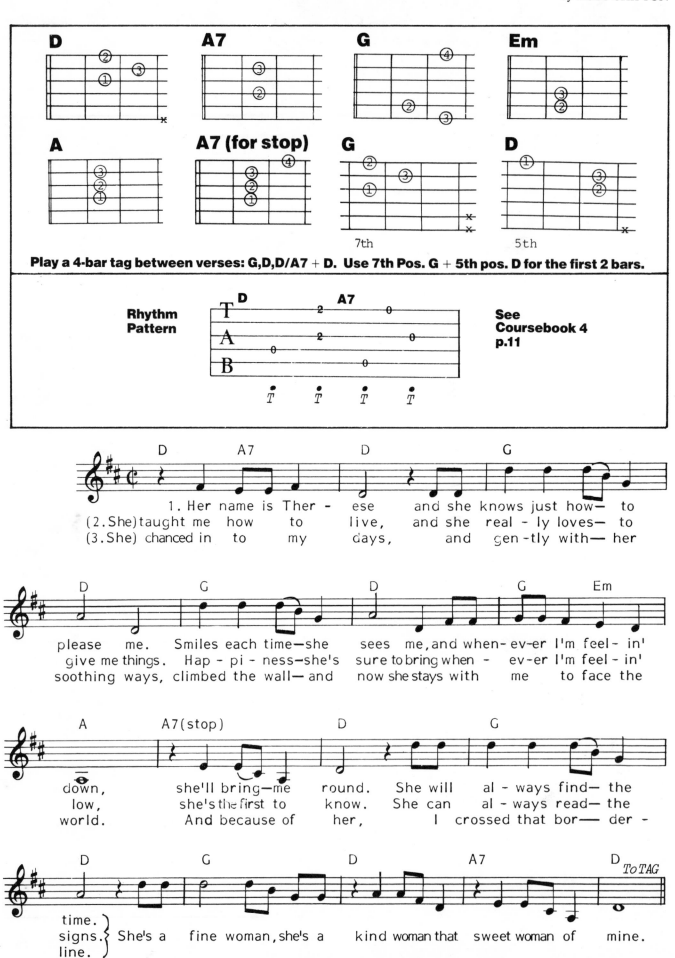